W.A.B.B.A.

World Amateur Body Builders' Association

Qualification

THE
ULTIMATE
WEIGHT - TRAINING
HANDBOOK

Alan Runacres

FCollP. FISM. BSc.(Hons). MNASC. Dip HMAN. MICM Dip

and

Scott Burton

MCollP, DMS. BA(Hons). Dip HMAN. M.Inst. SRM (Dip)

The publisher wishes to point out that this work has been produced by faithfuly producing information which has been verified by consultants and lecturers in the subject area. The information published is as accurate as possible at the time of going to press.

The publisher cannot be held responsible for any errors that may be found, or that may occur at some time in the future owing to changes in technical legislation, or for other reasons.

This is the first edition of The Ultimate Weight-Training Handbook and the first book published in the forthcoming "Ultimate Series" of handbooks.

ISBN No. 0-9537849-0-8

Printed by Westgate Print, 17a Westgate, Sleaford, Lincs., NG34 7PJ
Photographs by JLB Graphics Design & Art Direction (UK) 0467 476757

CONTENTS

THE AUTHORS

Alan Runacres
FCollP. FISM. BSc.(Hons). MNASC. Dip HMAN. MICM Dip.

- Director of Training for WABBA Qualifications.
- Founder of WABBA's New Qualifications Structure.
- Fellow of the College of Preceptors.
- Fellow of the Institute for Supervision and Management.
- Younger Members Officer for the College of Preceptors.
- Senior Lecturer on WABBA Training Principles & Sports Science Courses.
- Author of Training Manuals and designer of Course Syllabuses for Organisations and Awarding Bodies' in the Fitness Industry.

Scott Burton
MCollP. DMS. BA (Hons). Dip HMAN. M.Inst.SRM (Dip).

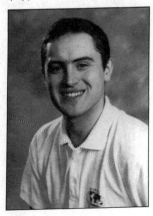

- Education Officer for WABBA Qualifications.
- Member of the College of Preceptors Teacher Training College.
- Became the Youngest I.S.R.M. Diploma Holder at the age of 20.
- Former Junior National Swimming Competitor.
- Lecturer on WABBA Training Principles & Sports Science Courses.
- Author of Training Manuals and Courses Syllabuses for Organisations and Awarding Bodies' in the Fitness Industry.

ACKNOWLEDGEMENTS

Nick Wright
Dip HMAN. 4th Dan.

- Training Officer for WABBA Qualifications.
- WABBA Qualifications Tutor Panel Member.
- Senior Lecturer on WABBA Flexibility Studies Courses.
- Senior National Squad Coach for Bushido Kai Karate (UK).
- Personal Trainer.

Wendy Ogilvie
Dip HMAN

- Senior National Assessor for WABBA Qualifications.
- WABBA Qualifications Tutor Panel Member.
- Lecturer on WABBA Training Principles and Sports Science Courses.
- WABBA "Instructor of the Year" Finalist 1996.
- WABBA UK Bodybuilding Judge.
- Personal Trainer.

ACKNOWLEDGEMENTS

Ian Minor
Dip HMAN

- Co-ordination Officer for WABBA Qualifications.
- WABBA Assessor Team Member.
- WABBA Qualifications Tutor Panel Member.
- Senior Lecturer on WABBA Fitness Assessment Courses.
- Personal Trainer.

Tarik Elmetaal
Dip HMAN

- WABBA Assessor Team Member.
- WABBA Qualifications Tutor Panel Member.
- Lecturer on WABBA Flexibility Studies Courses.
- Personal Trainer.

ACKNOWLEDGEMENTS

Lisa Hayes
Dip HMAN

- WABBA Assessor Team Member.
- WABBA Qualifications Tutor Panel Member.
- Lecturer on WABBA Weight-Training Practical Skills Courses.
- Personal Trainer.

James Bird
Dip HMAN

- WABBA Assessor Team Member.
- WABBA Qualifications Tutor Panel Member.
- Lecturer on WABBA Weight-Training Practical Skills Courses.
- Personal Trainer.

ACKNOWLEDGEMENTS

Joanna Lunn
Dip HMAN

- WABBA Assessor Team Member.
- WABBA "Instructor of the Year" Finalist 1996.
- Sports Massage Therapist.
- Personal Trainer.

John Tansey
Dip HMAN

- WABBA Assessor Team Member.
- WABBA "Instructor of the Year" Finalist 1997.
- WABBA Qualifications Tutor Panel Member.
- Lecturer on WABBA Weight-Training Practical Skills Courses.
- Personal Trainer.

ACKNOWLEDGEMENTS

Julie Mabe
RSA

- WABBA "Instructor of the Year" Finalist 1996.
- Exercise to Music Teacher.
- Sports Massage Therapist.
- Personal Trainer.

Martin and Pamela Ruffell

Founders of the:
Paradise Health & Fitness Centre
Rainham
Essex
Great Britain

Alan and Scott would like to take this opportunity to thank Martin & Pam for their assistance in the production of this book.

Preface

Traditionally the gymnasium was a place frequented by dedicated weight trainers and physical culturists (usually referred to as Bodybuilders) who were introduced into the art of using barbells and machinery for gains in strength and size by already very experienced participants of this culture, who had a tremendous depth of background knowledge.

However, this is not the case anymore, since the onset of the fitness revolution in the 1990's the popularity of gymnasiums and health and fitness clubs has rocketed to an all-time high, with the public demand for experienced teachers outstripping the supply of knowledgeable people.

This has led to such a "watering-down" of weight-training knowledge and skills, that in most fitness clubs today, the majority of people training there are often either using the wrong exercise programmes, or incorrect training techniques.

WABBA Qualifications have set an unequalled benchmark with their Instructor Training and Education Programmes, and have launched this book to reveal the truth behind the secrets of weight-training.

With this book you have the first-hand knowledge of which exercises to choose for each area of your body according to your own training goals and abilities.

Whether an aspiring weight trainer, body builder or fitness instructor, now you have the "Ultimate" source of weight-training knowledge.

PLEASE READ CAREFULLY

Before starting any type of exercise programme you should always consult your physician to make sure that you are medically fit enough to undertake the programme.

The authors and WABBA will not be held responsible for any results, injuries or mishaps which occur either indirectly or directly as a result of reading this book.

INTRODUCTION

Dependent upon which kind of gymnasium or health and fitness club you attend, you will encounter numerous types of fitness and weight trainer, from the casual user to the dedicated athlete, particularly in the larger clubs and gymnasiums. Typically trainers fall into one of three types of category:

a) Leisure Trainers

Those people which attend fitness training sessions on average 2-3 times a week, for approximately 45 - 60 minute work-out sessions of either aerobic or gymnasium - based cardiovascular and resistance machine-based activities.

b) Sports Trainers

Generally sports trainers adapt their work-outs to enhance their sporting performance, which will usually mean that their work-outs will be structured predominantly around exercises that mimic the movements of their sporting activities.

c) Specialist Trainers

Many of the larger gymnasiums and fitness training facilities are now frequented by people pursuing exercise programmes dedicated to either strength training or bodybuilding to some degree, either at a level for personal improvement or to a competitive standard.

Athletes requiring explosive power also come into this category of generic trainer, who are far more dedicated to achieving their end goals than some of the lesser-motivated trainers who attend fitness centres and gymnasiums.

Training To Reach Your Goal

In order to achieve any level of sustained increase in fitness / strength, or increased muscular development you must ensure that you do not either undertrain or indeed overtrain your body, but ensure that your workouts are structured to provide you with what is known as Progressive Overload.

There are many theories concerning the amount of sets and repetitions that should be performed to achieve a target result in resistance training compared to the amount of weight that you are lifting. In order to ensure that you work at the correct level of resistance it is best to train at a percentage of what is known as your Power Maximum.

Finding Your Power Maximum

On exercises which are mainly considered to be compound movements ie; an exercise which uses several muscle groups at one time in the primary sense (see Primary and Secondary muscles highlighted on each exercise described) it is possible to test yourself safely on the amount of weight that you can lift as a safe maximum effort on one repetition.

This weight will be known as your **1 Repetition Power Maximum (1 RPM).**
Begin by lifting a weight for one rep in comfort and then add more and more weight in stages after each single repetition until you reach a point of failure. The last weight that you successfully lifted in strict style is the weight that is known as your 1 RPM.

On exercises which are isolation versions ie; they have only one main muscle group being worked, for example Dumbell Raises for shoulders or Dumbell Flyes for chest, extreme care must be taken not to sustain an injury from high stress loading on a single muscle group, and in particular for testing 1 RPM's.

Once you have been tested for your Power Maximums on the exercises you intend to use in your training program, you will be able to use the sets and repetitions table (**The WABBA Workload,** p.20) to tell you how many times you should lift a given percentage of your Power Maximum to obtain the result you require. This will take out the guess work that traditionally has been the background of the weight training arena.

At any time you cannot achieve the sets and repetitions recommended for your training result, then take some weight off the bars or machine that you are using to allow you to complete your given task. It is reasonable to assume that, dependent on your own level of progress you will need to re-test your Power Maximums every 8-12 weeks as your natural strength levels will have increased, which will ultimately lead to you training at a lesser level of intensity than you require. It is also important to vary your routine by replacing and/or adding different exercises to your training programme every 8-12 weeks.

Breathing

There are many schools of thought on which breathing technique to use when weight-training, but for most trainers all exercises will be performed under the guidelines of breathing in before you lift the weight and breathing out as you lift the weight, followed by breathing in again as you lower the weight back down to the starting position.

Certain exercises depicted in this book which are usually performed by bodybuilding enthusiasts require you to breathe the opposite way whilst performing them and this is clearly explained under the text heading **'THE ACTION'**.

How To Use This Book

* Read about 1 RPM 's and sets and reps.

* Understand the correct breathing techique for weight-training.

* Turn to a muscle group heading and select an appropriate number of exercises for your level of training.

* Ensure the exercises give the right results you are looking for before undertaking them.

* Always train carefully on new exercises giving yourself time to become accustomed to the movements involved.

* If in any doubt whatsoever about;

   1 RPM testing

   Sets and reps to use

   % of 1 RPM's to use

   Exercise choices and how often to train

   Then always consult a WABBA Fitness Instructor for advice.

How Many Exercises Should I Do?

a) Beginner's Programme

* Warm up on a bike or similar.
* Light mobility stretching of the muscles
* One main exercise for each major body part.
* Always train Abdominals afterwards, using 2-3 sets of 1 exercise to reasonable failure.
* Do a cool-down on a bike or similar.
* Carry out a post-workout stretching routine.
* Maintain your fluid intake before, during and after training.
* Eat or drink carbohydrate-based food/fluid immediately afterwards.

b) Intermediate Programme

* To be carried out by trainers having completed at least 8 - 12 weeks of continuous training on a beginner's programme with 2 - 3 training sessions completed each week.
* Warm up on a stepper, treadmill, stairmaster or similar. Starting off at a low level of intensity programme, due to the step-up in the degree of difficulty compared to a basic bike exercise programme.
* Stay on the beginners warm-up equipment if you struggle with aerobic fitness (ie: you still run out of breathe easily or find it hard to maintain aerobic exercise for longer than 15 - 20 minutes at a reasonable pace).
* Light mobility stretching of the muscles.
* Two exercises for each major body part (chest, back, shoulders, front legs, back of legs).
* 1-2 exercises for each smaller body part (arms, calves, forearms etc.) as deemed comfortable in meeting your requirements.
* Always train Abdominals afterwards, using 2-3 sets of 1-2 exercises to reasonable failure.
* Do a cool-down on a bike or similar.
* Carry out a post-workout stretching routine.
* Maintain your fluid intake before, during and after training.
* Eat or drink carbohydrate-based food/fluid immediately afterwards.

c) Advanced Programme

* Advanced training should only be undertaken by people with at least 9 months to a year's continuous training experience.
* Warm up on a rower, versa-climber or similar.
* Light mobility stretching of the muscles.
* Several exercises for each major body part plus 2 exercises for smaller body parts.
* Train on a split-routine ie: training only part of your body each day until you have completed all muscle groups after 3-4 days.
* Abdominals 2-3 sets of 2 or more exercises to reasonable failure on each or alternate training days at the end of the routine.
* Cool-down on a bike / treadmill or similar.
* Carry out a post-workout stretching routine.
* Maintain your fluid intake before, during and after training.
* Eat or drink carbohydrate-based food/fluid immediately afterwards in conjunction with Amino Acid supplementation.

Training Tip:

* The Abdominal muscles are used in over 90% of all exercises performed in the gym. By training them at the end of your exercise programme, you will not detract from other muscle group training performances.

This book has been written by dedicated practitioners of exercise science - but has been created to allow it's readers the opportunity of gaining not only quality results from their training, but also a sense of achievement and enjoyment from their sporting pastime.

ANATOMY (Frontal View)

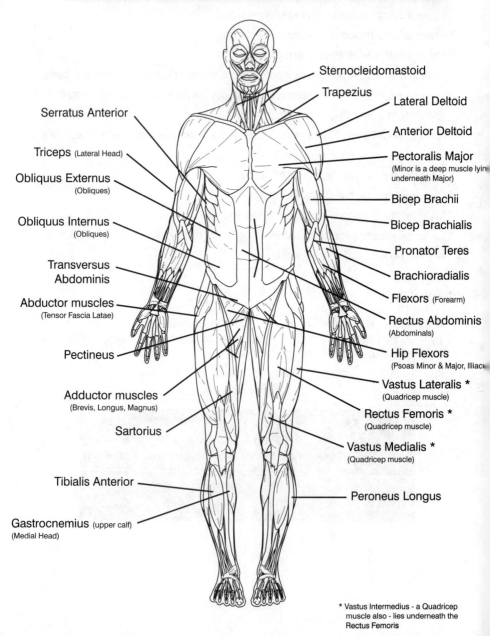

Sternocleidomastoid

Trapezius

Lateral Deltoid

Serratus Anterior

Anterior Deltoid

Triceps (Lateral Head)

Pectoralis Major
(Minor is a deep muscle lyin
underneath Major)

Obliquus Externus
(Obliques)

Bicep Brachii

Obliquus Internus
(Obliques)

Bicep Brachialis

Pronator Teres

Transversus
Abdominis

Brachioradialis

Abductor muscles
(Tensor Fascia Latae)

Flexors (Forearm)

Rectus Abdominis
(Abdominals)

Pectineus

Hip Flexors
(Psoas Minor & Major, Illiac

Adductor muscles
(Brevis, Longus, Magnus)

Vastus Lateralis *
(Quadricep muscle)

Rectus Femoris *
(Quadricep muscle)

Sartorius

Vastus Medialis *
(Quadricep muscle)

Tibialis Anterior

Peroneus Longus

Gastrocnemius (upper calf)
(Medial Head)

* Vastus Intermedius - a Quadricep
muscle also - lies underneath the
Rectus Femoris

ANATOMY (Rear View)

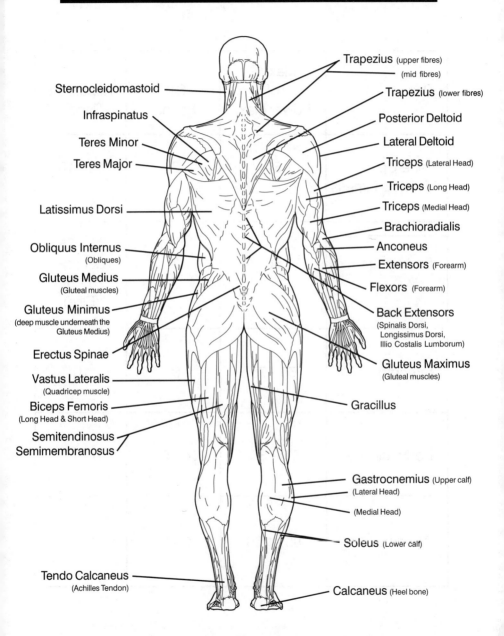

Sternocleidomastoid

Infraspinatus

Teres Minor

Teres Major

Latissimus Dorsi

Obliquus Internus
(Obliques)

Gluteus Medius
(Gluteal muscles)

Gluteus Minimus
(deep muscle underneath the
Gluteus Medius)

Erectus Spinae

Vastus Lateralis
(Quadricep muscle)

Biceps Femoris
(Long Head & Short Head)

Semitendinosus
Semimembranosus

Tendo Calcaneus
(Achilles Tendon)

Trapezius (upper fibres)
(mid fibres)

Trapezius (lower fibres)

Posterior Deltoid

Lateral Deltoid

Triceps (Lateral Head)

Triceps (Long Head)

Triceps (Medial Head)

Brachioradialis

Anconeus

Extensors (Forearm)

Flexors (Forearm)

Back Extensors
(Spinalis Dorsi,
Longissimus Dorsi,
Illio Costalis Lumborum)

Gluteus Maximus
(Gluteal muscles)

Gracillus

Gastrocnemius (Upper calf)
(Lateral Head)
(Medial Head)

Soleus (Lower calf)

Calcaneus (Heel bone)

THE WABBA WORKLOAD

Result	Max. % of Power Max.	Set Range	Repetition Range
Tone-Up General Fitness	50	2	12 - 15
Endurance	60	3	15 - 25 (General) 25 - 50 (Elite)
Strength	70 - 75	3	10
Bodybuilding	70 - 85	4 - 6	8 - 12
Powerbuilding	85 - 100	3 - 5	1 - 6

TRAINING TIPS

BENCHES:	1. Ensure that your back remains flat against the pads for support whenever possible. 2. For "Incline" work, always set the bench at a low angle - usually between 1 or 2 settings up from "flat", which will allow you to work at an angle of somewhere in the region of 30 degrees. NB: Go NO Higher than 45 degrees for "Incline" work. 3. Try whenever possible to keep both feet flat on the floor with your legs kept still during exercise execution. (If your back begins to arch away from the bench support pads you may have to put both feet up onto the bench to allow the correct position to be assumed).
HANDGRIPS:	For safety, it is recommended at all times to adopt the "Classical" grip, with both the fingers and thumbs wrapped around the bars and handles of equipment that you are using in the gym.
FRENCHGRIPS:	An advanced training technique, where you remove the thumbs off from around the bars and handles of the equipment, relying solely on the fingers and palms of the hand for grip and safety. NB: This should not be attempted by anyone who has a limited amount of experience in Advanced Weight-Training & Bodybuilding Techniques.
SAFETY COLLARS:	Always put safety collars on training bars to hold the weight discs in place whilst you exercise. Lock them securely against the last disc that you put on each end of the bar.
SPEED:	Never train as if you were in a race, execute each repetition in a safe and controlled manner, taking an average count of 2 before you reach either the start or finish position of any training movement.

W.A.B.B.A. QUALIFICATIONS
AWARDS STRUCTURE

The levels of awards illustrated below, will give you a clearer picture of the progression that can be made within the Association's Instructor Education Programme. All Senior WABBA Qualifications Officers and Assessors have themselves successfully progressed through the various levels of the Awards Structure, having learned the practical skills and theoretical knowledge given to you in this book.

FITNESS INSTRUCTOR CERTIFICATE
ADVANCED FITNESS ASSESSMENTS **FLEXIBILITY STUDIES** **NUTRITION** **ADVANCED WEIGHT - TRAINING SKILLS** **ADVANCED FITNESS PROGRAMME WRITING**
SENIOR FITNESS INSTRUCTOR CERTIFICATE
CERTIFICATE IN HEALTH MANAGEMENT (Cert HMAN)
DIPLOMA IN HEALTH MANAGEMENT (Dip HMAN)
WABBA ASSESSOR
WABBA COACH / COURSE TUTOR
WABBA SENIOR COACH / SENIOR TUTOR
WABBA STAFF COACH / LECTURER
EXECUTIVE COACHING PANEL MEMBER
DIRECTOR OF TRAINING

W.A.B.B.A.
NATIONAL TRAINING CENTRES
OF EXCELLENCE

The WABBA Qualifications Instructor Education Programme is delivered by Recognised Training Providers of the Association's Awards Structure. These awards are obtainable through leading Colleges and Fitness Centres which hold the prestigious WABBA National Training Centre of Excellence Certificate.

This enables them to deliver part or all of the WABBA Awards structure, dependent upon their own resources. For further information, contact either your local College to see if they hold Centre of Excellence Status, or contact WABBA direct at:-

WABBA QUALIFICATIONS
LINDUM HOUSE
NORTHGATE
SLEAFORD
LINCS
NG34 7BX
GREAT BRITAIN

TEL / FAX: + 44 (0)1529 - 303 - 259

Successful WABBA students all agree on one thing - The Course Structures are Second To None. Look at what they say;

"Excellent progressive learning strategies on courses, which are the best"

"The style of teaching is unbeatable"

"Learned more in a week, than in a full year on my Honours Degree Programme"

"The courses are fun, informative, and very challenging"

"WABBA are surely The Number 1 Choice"

All of our testimonials and course evaluations are kept on file and are open to inspection by prior arranged appointment.

PRIMARY & SECONDARY MUSCLES

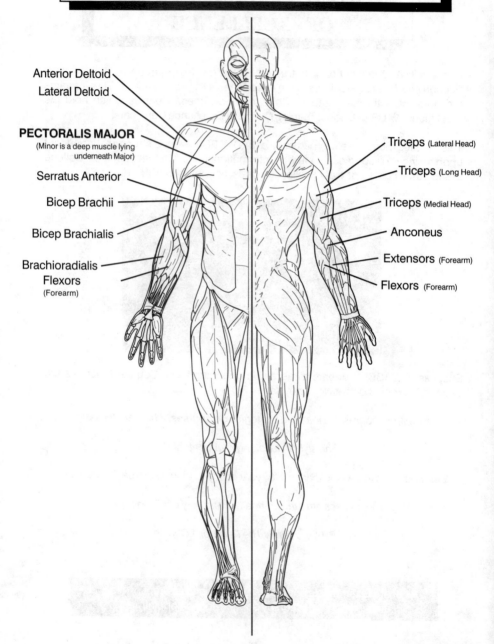

Anterior Deltoid
Lateral Deltoid

PECTORALIS MAJOR
(Minor is a deep muscle lying
underneath Major)

Serratus Anterior

Bicep Brachii

Bicep Brachialis

Brachioradialis
Flexors
(Forearm)

Triceps (Lateral Head)

Triceps (Long Head)

Triceps (Medial Head)

Anconeus

Extensors (Forearm)

Flexors (Forearm)

CHEST
EXERCISES

DECLINE DUMBELL FLYES

THE SCIENCE

Muscles used:	
Primary:	The lower Pectoral chest muscles (Pectoralis Major and Minor).
Secondary:	The front shoulder (Anterior Deltoid) muscles and to a lesser degree the Lateral Deltoid, Serratus Anterior, Bicep arm muscles, and forearm muscles.
The Result:	Predominantly a shaping exercise for the lower chest.
Who is it for?: Men + Women:	Involved in bodybuilding programmes.
The Training Zone:	Bodybuilding: 4-6 sets of 8-12 reps.

THE ACTION

How To Do It:	1) Select a weight which allows you to perform your target Training Zone in a safe and controlled manner.
	2) Now lie down onto the bench, bringing the dumbells off from being supported on the thighs to the sides of the chest. Simultaneously press both dumbells up from the wide base of your chest width to a point centrally located above the mid-chest when the arms are fully extended and turn the palms of your hands in to face each other.
	3) Now bend the arms slightly and lock the elbows. Whilst breathing in, allow the dumbells to go out in an arc away from the central line above the body, finishing when the dumbells are outstretched, elbows still bent, creating a full stretch onto the Pectoral chest muscles.
	4) From this position, draw the dumbells back on the same arc finishing at the peak of the movement over the chest where you began whilst breathing out.
	5) Ensure the palms of both hands remain inwards throughout the entire movement facing each other.

Start Position:

Finish Position:

INCLINE DUMBELL FLYES

	THE SCIENCE
Muscles used:	
Primary:	The upper Pectoral chest muscles (Pectoralis Major and Minor).
Secondary:	The front shoulder (Anterior Deltoid) muscles and to a lesser degree the Lateral Deltoid, Serratus Anterior, Bicep arm muscles, and forearm muscles.
The Result:	Predominantly a shaping exercise for the upper chest.
Who is it for?: Men + Women:	Involved in muscle toning and/or bodybuilding exercise programmes.
The Training Zone:	Muscle Tone: 2-3 sets of 12-15 reps. Bodybuilding: 4-6 sets of 8-12 reps.

	THE ACTION
How To Do It:	1) Select a weight which allows you to perform your target Training Zone in a safe and controlled manner.
	2) Now lie down onto the bench, bringing the dumbells off from being supported on the thighs to the sides of the chest. Simultaneously press both dumbells up from the wide base of your chest width to a point centrally located above the mid-chest when the arms are fully extended and turn the palms of your hands in to face each other.
	3) Now bend the arms slightly and lock the elbows. Whilst breathing in, allow the dumbells to go out in an arc away from the central line above the body, finishing when the dumbells are outstretched, elbows still bent, creating a full stretch onto the Pectoral chest muscles.
	4) From this position, draw the dumbells back in on the same arc finishing at the peak of the movement above your chest whilst breathing out.
	5) Ensure the palms of both hands remain inwards throughout the entire movement facing each other.

Start Position:

Finish Position:

FLAT DUMBELL FLYES

THE SCIENCE

Muscles used:	
Primary:	The Pectoral chest muscles (Pectoralis Major and Minor).
Secondary:	The front shoulder (Anterior Deltoid) muscles and to a lesser degree the Lateral Deltoid, Serratus Anterior, Bicep arm muscles, and forearm muscles.
The Result:	Predominantly a shaping exercise for the mid-chest.
Who is it for?: Men + Women:	Involved in muscle toning and/or bodybuilding exercise programmes.
The Training Zone:	Muscle Tone: 2-3 sets of 12-15 reps. Bodybuilding: 4-6 sets of 8-12 reps.

THE ACTION

How To Do It:	1) Select a weight which allows you to perform your target Training Zone in a safe and controlled manner.
	2) Now lie down onto the bench, bringing the dumbells off from being supported on the thighs to the sides of the chest. Simultaneously press both dumbells up from the wide base of your chest width to a point centrally located above the mid-chest when the arms are fully extended and turn the palms of your hands in to face each other.
	3) Now bend the arms slightly and lock the elbows. Whilst breathing in, allow the dumbells to go out in an arc away from the central line above the body, finishing when the dumbells are outstretched, elbows still bent, creating a full stretch onto the Pectoral chest muscles.
	4) From this position, draw the dumbells back in on the same arc finishing at the peak of the movement above your chest whilst breathing out.
	5) Ensure the palms of both hands remain inwards throughout the entire movement facing each other.

Start Position:

Finish Position:

CABLE CROSSOVERS

THE SCIENCE

Muscles used:	
Primary:	The Pectoral chest muscles (Pectoralis Major and Minor).
Secondary:	The front shoulder (Anterior Deltoid) muscles, and to a lesser degree the Lateral Deltoid, Bicep arm muscles and forearm muscles.
The Result:	An exercise for either mid to upper chest or mid to lower chest shaping, dependant upon the finishing position of the hands throughout the movement.
Who is it for?: Men:	Already having basic chest muscle development, who require additional shape and definition.
Women:	Requiring additional toning and shaping of the chest.
The Training Zone:	Muscle Tone: 2-3 sets of 12-15 reps. Bodybuilding: 4-6 sets of 8-12 reps.

THE ACTION

How To Do It:	1) Select a weight which allows you to perform your target Training Zone in a safe and controlled manner.
	2) For upper chest work, take hold of both handles and step slightly forward to the front of the machine, using a "flye" movement to take the handles from the sides of the body ($^3/_4$ outstretched) to a finishing position with the elbows still locked in a slightly bent position, hands at upper chest height with the arms parallel to the ground.
	3) For lower chest work, use a "flye" movement to take the arms from a $^3/_4$ outstretched position from the sides of the body down to a finishing position in front of the lower abdominal region, still maintaining the elbows in a bent and locked position throughout.
	4) Both techniques require you to breathe in at the outstretched starting position and out as you approach the finishing position.

Start Position: (mid to lower chest)

Finish Position: (mid to lower chest)

Start Position: (mid to upper chest)

Finish Position: (mid to upper chest)

DECLINE DUMBELL PRESS

THE SCIENCE

Muscles used:	
Primary:	The lower Pectoral chest muscles (Pectoralis Major and Minor).
Secondary:	The Tricep arm muscles, the front and side shoulder (Anterior and Lateral Deltoid) muscles and to a lesser degree the Serratus Anterior, forearm and Anconeus muscles.
The Result:	A strength and mass-building exercise for the lower chest.
Who is it for?: Men + Women:	Involved in strength building, bodybuilding and powerbuilding exercise programmes.
The Training Zone:	Strength: 3 sets of 10 reps. Bodybuilding: 4-6 sets of 8-12 reps. Powerbuilding: 3-5 sets of 1-6 reps.

THE ACTION

How To Do It:	1) Select a weight which allows you to perform your target Training Zone in a safe and controlled manner.
	2) Now lie down onto the bench, bringing the dumbells off from being supported on the thighs to the sides of the chest. Simultaneously press both dumbells up from the wide base of your chest width to a point centrally located above the mid-chest when the arms are fully extended.
	3) This pressing action finishes at the peak of an imaginary "pyramid" at which you breathe out before lowering the dumbells back down to the wide base (your side chest) whilst breathing in.
	4) Ensure the palms of both hands remain facing forwards throughout the entire movement.

Start Position:

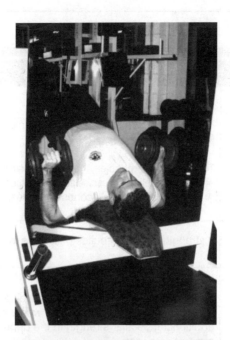

Finish Position:

INCLINE DUMBELL PRESS

THE SCIENCE

Muscles used:	
Primary:	The upper Pectoral chest muscles (Pectoralis Major and Minor).
Secondary:	The Tricep arm muscles, the front and side shoulder (Anterior and Lateral Deltoid) muscles and to a lesser degree the Serratus Anterior, forearm and Anconeus muscles.
The Result:	A strength and mass-building exercise for the upper chest.
Who is it for?: Men + Women:	Involved in strength building, bodybuilding and powerbuilding exercise programmes, together with women who require additional muscular strength in the upper chest regions for support purposes.
The Training Zone:	Strength: 3 sets of 10 reps. Bodybuilding: 4-6 sets of 8 12 reps. Powerbuilding: 3-5 sets of 1-6 reps.

THE ACTION

How To Do It:	1) Select a weight which allows you to perform your target Training Zone in a safe and controlled manner.
	2) Now lie down onto the bench, bringing the dumbells off from being supported on the thighs to the sides of the chest. Simultaneously press both dumbells up from the wide base of your chest width to a point centrally located above the mid-chest when the arms are fully extended.
	3) This pressing action finishes at the peak of an imaginary "pyramid" at which you breathe out before lowering the dumbells back down to the wide base (your side chest) whilst breathing in.
	4) Ensure the palms of both hands remain facing forwards throughout the entire movement.

Start Position:

Finish Position:

Start Position:

Finish Position:

FLAT DUMBELL PRESS

THE SCIENCE

Muscles used:	
Primary:	The Pectoral chest muscles (Pectoralis Major and Minor).
Secondary:	The Tricep arm muscles, the front and side shoulder (Anterior and Lateral Deltoid) muscles and to a lesser degree the Serratus Anterior, forearm and Anconeus muscles.
The Result:	A strength and mass-building exercise for the mid-chest.
Who is it for?: Men + Women:	Involved in strength building, bodybuilding and powerbuilding exercise programmes.
The Training Zone:	Strength: 3 sets of 10 reps. Bodybuilding: 4-6 sets of 8-12 reps. Powerbuilding: 3-5 sets of 1-6 reps.

THE ACTION

How To Do It:	1) Select a weight which allows you to perform your target Training Zone in a safe and controlled manner.
	2) Now lie down onto a flat bench, bringing the dumbells off from being supported on the thighs to the sides of the chest. Simultaneously press both dumbells up from the wide base of your chest width to a point centrally located above the mid-chest when the arms are fully extended.
	3) This pressing action finishes at the peak of an imaginary "pyramid" at which you breathe out before lowering the dumbells back down to the wide base (your side chest) whilst breathing in.
	4) Ensure the palms of both hands remain facing forwards throughout the entire movement.

Start Position:

Finish Position:

DECLINE BARBELL PRESS

THE SCIENCE

Muscles used:	
Primary:	The lower Pectoral chest muscles (Pectoralis Major and Minor).
Secondary:	The Tricep arm muscles, the front and side shoulder (Anterior and Lateral Deltoid) muscles and to a lesser degree the Serratus Anterior, forearm and Anconeus muscles.
The Result:	A strength and mass-building exercise for the lower chest.
Who Is It For? Men + Women:	Involved in strength building, bodybuilding and powerbuilding exercise programmes.
The Training Zone:	Strength: 3 sets of 10 reps. Bodybuilding: 4-6 sets of 8-12 reps. Powerbuilding: 3-5 sets of 1-6 reps.

THE ACTION

How To Do It:	1) Select a weight which allows you to perform your target Training Zone in a safe and controlled manner.
	2) Now lie down onto the bench, taking a grip on the bar just past shoulder width and bring the barbell away from the bench supports to a position over the mid-chest line with the arms fully extended and breathe out.
	3) Lower the bar down to the chest as you breathe in by bending the elbows, and finishing with the bar touching the chest just below the middle section.
	4) Now breathe out and press out until your arms are fully extended.

Start Position:

Finish Position:

INCLINE BARBELL PRESS

THE SCIENCE

Muscles used:	
Primary:	The upper Pectoral chest muscles (Pectoralis Major and Minor).
Secondary:	The Tricep arm muscles and the front and side shoulder (Anterior and Lateral Deltoid) muscles and to a lesser degree the Serratus Anterior, forearm and Anconeus muscles.
The Result:	A strength and mass-building exercise for the upper chest.
Who Is It For? Men + Women:	Involved in strength building, bodybuilding and powerbuilding exercise programmes.
The Training Zone:	Strength: 3 sets of 10 reps. Bodybuilding: 4-6 sets of 8-12 reps. Powerbuilding: 3-5 sets of 1-6 reps.

THE ACTION

How To Do It:

1) Select a weight which allows you to perform your target Training Zone in a safe and controlled manner.

2) Now lie down onto the bench, taking a grip on the bar just past shoulder width and bring the barbell away from the bench supports to a position over the mid-chest line with the arms fully extended and breathe out.

3) Lower the bar down to the chest as you breathe in by bending the elbows and finishing with the bar touching the chest just above the middle section.

4) Now breathe out and press out until your arms are fully extended.

Start Position:

Finish Position:

INCLINE CHEST PRESS MACHINE

Muscles used:	
Primary:	The upper Pectoral chest muscles (Pectoralis Major and Minor).
Secondary:	The Tricep arm muscles, the front and side shoulder (Anterior and Lateral Deltoid) muscles, and to a lesser degree the Serratus Anterior, forearm and Anconeus muscles.
The Result:	A strength and mass-building exercise for the upper chest.
Who Is It For? Men + Women:	Involved in muscle toning and/or strength building or bodybuilding exercise programmes.
The Training Zone:	Muscle Tone: 2-3 sets of 12-15 reps. Strength: 3 sets of 10 reps. Bodybuilding: 4-6 sets of 8-12 reps.

THE ACTION

How To Do It:

1) Select a weight which allows you to perform your target Training Zone in a safe and controlled manner.

2) Position seat height so that the handles are in line with the mid to upper chest line.

3) Place your feet onto the footplate and press the lever forwards.

4) Grasp the handles, which are now in line with your chest.

5) Release your feet from the lever taking the strain onto the arms.

6) Now breathe out and press out until your arms are fully extended.

7) Slowly return the handles to the side-chest line whilst breathing in.

8) Upon completion of your repetitions, use the foot lever to allow you to return the handles to their starting position.

Start Position:

Finish Position:

INCLINE CHEST PRESS (SMITHS MACHINE)

THE SCIENCE

Muscles used:	
Primary:	The upper Pectoral chest muscles (Pectoralis Major and Minor).
Secondary:	The Tricep arm muscles, the front and side shoulder (Anterior and Lateral Deltoid) muscles, and to a lesser degree the Serratus Anterior, forearm and Anconeus muscles.
The Result:	A strength and mass-building exercise for the upper chest.
Who Is It For? Men + Women:	Involved in strength building, bodybuilding, and powerbuilding exercise programmes.
The Training Zone:	Strength: 3 sets of 10 reps. Bodybuilding: 4-6 sets of 8-12 reps. Powerbuilding: 3-5 sets of 1-6 reps.

THE ACTION

How To Do It:	1) Select a weight which allows you to perform your target Training Zone in a safe and controlled manner.
	2) Position yourself onto an inclined bench (30°-45°).
	3) Ensure your back is flat onto the bench.
	4) Position your hands slightly wider than shoulder width apart on the bar.
	5) Extend the arms fully, unlocking the bar's safety catches by slightly rotating your wrists.
	6) Lower the bar down to the chest as you breathe in by bending the elbows and finishing with the bar touching the chest just above the middle section.
	7) Now breathe out and press out until your arms are fully extended, "locking-on" the safety catches upon completion of the exercise set of repetitions.

Start Position:

Finish Position:

FLAT BARBELL PRESS

THE SCIENCE

Muscles used:	
Primary:	The Pectoral chest muscles (Pectoralis Major and Minor).
Secondary:	The Tricep arm muscles, the front and side shoulder (Anterior and Lateral Deltoid) muscles and to a lesser degree the Serratus Anterior, forearm and Anconeus muscles.
The Result:	A strength and mass-building exercise for the mid-chest.
Who Is It For? Men + Women:	Involved in strength building, bodybuilding, and powerbuilding exercise programmes.
The Training Zone:	Strength: 3 sets of 10 reps. Bodybuilding: 4-6 sets of 8-12 reps. Powerbuilding: 3-5 sets of 1-6 reps.

THE ACTION

How To Do It:	1) Select a weight which allows you to perform your target Training Zone in a safe and controlled manner. 2) Now lie down onto a flat bench, taking a grip on the bar just past shoulder width and bring the barbell away from the bench supports to a position over the mid-chest line with the arms fully extended and breathe out. 3) Lower the bar down to the chest as you breathe in by bending the elbows and finishing with the bar touching the chest just above the middle section. 4) Now breathe out and press out until your arms are fully extended.

Start Position:

Finish Position:

LYING CHEST PRESS (SMITHS MACHINE)

THE SCIENCE

Muscles used:	
Primary:	The Pectoral chest muscles (Pectoralis Major and Minor).
Secondary:	The Tricep arm muscles, the front and side shoulder (Anterior and Lateral Deltoid) muscles, and to a lesser degree the Serratus Anterior, forearm and Anconeus muscles.
The Result:	A strength and mass-building exercise for the mid chest.
Who Is It For? Men + Women:	Involved in strength building, bodybuilding, and powerbuilding exercise programmes.
The Training Zone:	Strength: 3 sets of 10 reps. Bodybuilding: 4-6 sets of 8-12 reps. Powerbuilding: 3-5 sets of 1-6 reps.

THE ACTION

How To Do It?	1) Select a weight which allows you to perform your target Training Zone in a safe and controlled manner.
	2) Lie on a flat bench with your feet flat onto the floor.
	3) Ensure your back is flat onto the bench with the bar positioned over the mid-chest line.
	4) Position your hands slightly wider than shoulder width apart on the bar.
	5) Extend the arms fully, unlocking the bar's safety catches by slightly rotating your wrists.
	6) Lower the bar down to the chest as you breathe in by bending the elbows and finishing with the bar touching the chest just above the middle section.
	7) Now breathe out and press out until your arms are fully extended, "locking-on" the safety catches upon completion of the exercise set of repetitions.

Start Position:

Finish Position:

VERTICAL CHEST PRESS MACHINE

THE SCIENCE

Muscles used:	
Primarily:	The mid to lower or mid to upper Pectoral chest muscles (Pectoralis Major and Minor), subject to correct height adjustment of seat.
Secondary:	The Tricep arm muscles, the front and side shoulder (Anterior and Lateral Deltoid) muscles, and to a lesser degree the Serratus Anterior, forearm and Anconeus muscles.
The Result:	Generally an all-round strength and mass-building exercise for the chest, which can also be utilised for fitness training purposes.
Who Is It For? Men + Women:	Requiring a chest-building exercise utilising minimal technical ability. Suitable for general and specialist trainers.
The Training Zone:	Muscle Tone: 2-3 sets of 12-15 reps. Endurance: 3 sets of 15-25 reps or 25-50 reps Elite level. Strength: 3 sets of 10 reps. Bodybuilding: 4-6 sets of 8-12 reps.

THE ACTION

How To Do It:	1) Select a weight which allows you to perform your target Training Zone in a safe and controlled manner.
	2) Position seat height so that the handles are in line with the mid to lower or mid to upper chest line.
	3) Place your feet onto the footplate and press the lever forwards.
	4) Grasp the handles which are now in line with your chest.
	5) Release your feet from the lever taking the strain onto the arms.
	6) Now breathe out and press out until your arms are fully extended.
	7) Slowly return the handles to the side-chest line whilst breathing in.
	8) Upon completion of your repetitions, use the foot lever to allow you to return the handles to their starting position.

Start Position:

Finish Position:

I.B.S. CHEST PRESS

Muscles used:	
Primarily:	The mid to lower or mid to upper Pectoral chest muscles (Pectoralis Major and Minor), subject to correct height adjustment of seat.
Secondary:	The Tricep arm muscles, the front and side shoulder (Anterior and Lateral Deltoid) muscles, and to a lesser degree the Serratus Anterior, forearm and Anconeus muscles.
The Result:	Generally an all-round strength and mass-building exercise for the chest, which can also be utilised for fitness training purposes.
Who Is It For? Men + Women:	Involved in strength building, bodybuilding and powerbuilding exercise programmes.
The Training Zone:	Strength: 3 sets of 10 reps. Bodybuilding: 4-6 sets of 8-12 reps. Powerbuilding: 3-5 sets of 1-6 reps.

THE ACTION

How To Do It:	1) Select a weight which allows you to perform your target Training Zone in a safe and controlled manner. 2) Position seat height so that the handles are in line with the mid to lower or mid to upper chest line. 3) Place your feet flat onto the floor and grasp the handles which are now in line with your chest. 4) Now breathe out and press out until your arms are fully extended. 5) Slowly return the handles to the side-chest line whilst breathing in.

Start Position:

Finish Position:

PEC-DEC MACHINE

THE SCIENCE

Muscles used:	
Primarily:	The Pectoral chest muscles (Pectoralis Major and Minor) on both the outer edge and mid-line areas between both pec muscles.
Secondary:	The front and side (Anterior and Lateral Deltoid) shoulder muscles and to a lesser degree the Bicep arm (Brachialis) muscles and the forearm muscles.
The Result:	An isolation exercise providing excellent shaping and toning of the chest muscles.
Who Is It For? Men + Women:	Requiring a chest-shaping exercise utilising minimal technical ability. Suitable for general fitness and specialist trainers.
The Training Zone:	Muscle Tone: 2-3 sets of 12-15 reps. Endurance: 3 sets of 15-25 reps or 25-50 reps Elite level. Bodybuilding: 4-6 sets of 8-12 reps.

THE ACTION

How To Do It:	1) Select a weight which allows you to perform your target Training Zone in a safe and controlled manner.
	2) Adjust seat height so that your arms are bent at a right angle with your forearms on the pads provided, and upper arms parallel with the ground.
	3) Now breathe out as you squeeze your forearms together in front of you finishing with the pads in front of the centre of your chest.
	4) Ensure that your back remains flat against the support pad throughout the entire movement.
	5) Slowly return the arms to the starting position whilst breathing in.

Start Position:

Finish Position:

PRIMARY & SECONDARY MUSCLES

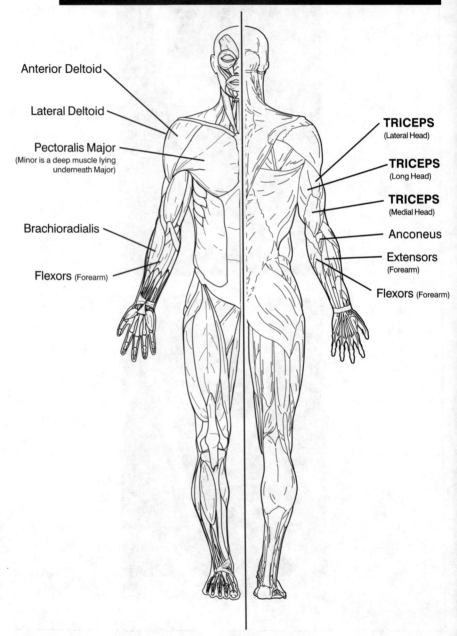

Anterior Deltoid

Lateral Deltoid

Pectoralis Major
(Minor is a deep muscle lying
underneath Major)

Brachioradialis

Flexors (Forearm)

TRICEPS
(Lateral Head)

TRICEPS
(Long Head)

TRICEPS
(Medial Head)

Anconeus

Extensors
(Forearm)

Flexors (Forearm)

TRICEP
EXERCISES

TRICEP PUSHDOWNS

THE SCIENCE

Muscles used:	
Primary:	The Tricep arm muscles (Lateral and Long Heads) in conjunction with the Medial Head to a lesser degree.
Secondary:	The forearm muscles, the shoulder muscles (Deltoids) and the Anconeus muscles.
The Result:	An exercise which is primarily used for shaping the Triceps but is also incorporated into bodybuilding programmes.
Who is it for?: Men + Women:	Involved in general fitness and/or bodybuilding programmes.
The Training Zone:	Muscle Tone: 2-3 sets of 12-15 reps. Bodybuilding: 4-6 sets of 8-12 reps.

THE ACTION

How to do it:	1) Select a weight which allows you to perform your target Training Zone in a safe and controlled manner.
	2) Take a narrow overhand grip with the hands approximately 8-10 inches apart on a flat bar and push the weight down until your arms are fully extended in front of your body. Ensure your upper arms remain tucked into the sides of your body as you bend your elbows and allow your forearms to come up a little past parallel to the floor whilst breathing in.
	3) Now push down with your hands as you breathe out and fully extend the arms back to the starting position whilst contracting the Triceps. By leaning the torso in towards the high cable, you can create a greater stretch on the Triceps at the top of the movement.
	4) Ensure you only lean forward with the trunk to a slight angle, avoiding use of the shoulders too much during the movement.

Start Position:

Finish Position:

TRICEP EXTENSION MACHINE

THE SCIENCE

Muscles used:	
Primarily:	The Tricep arm muscles (Long and Medial Heads).
Secondary:	The Lateral Head of the Triceps, the forearm and Anconeus muscles.
The Result:	An isolation exercise providing excellent shaping and building capabilities for the Triceps.
Who Is It For? Men + Women:	An excellent exercise requiring minimal technical ability, suitable for general and specialist trainers.
The Training Zone:	Muscle Tone: 2-3 sets of 12-15 reps. Bodybuilding: 4-6 sets of 8-12 reps.

THE ACTION

How To Do It:	1) Select a weight which allows you to perform your target Training Zone in a safe and controlled manner.
	2) Adjust the seat height so that your elbows are in line with the pivot point of the machine arm.
	3) Grasp the handles and push the backs of your upper arms onto the support pads.
	4) Breathe out whilst extending your arms out, fully pushing your hands away from you.
	5) Slowly return the handles back towards your front shoulders whilst breathing in.

Start Position:

Finish Position:

BARBELL CLOSE GRIP PRESS

THE SCIENCE

Muscles used:	
Primary:	The Tricep arm (Long, Medial & Lateral Head) muscles.
Secondary:	The front and side shoulder (Anterior and Lateral Deltoid) muscles, the Pectoral chest muscles, forearm and Anconeus muscles.
The Result:	A strength and mass-building exercise for the Tricep arm muscles.
Who Is It For? Men + Women:	Involved in strength building and bodybuilding exercise programmes.
The Training Zone:	Strength: 3 sets of 10 reps. Bodybuilding: 4-6 sets of 8-12 reps.

THE ACTION

How To Do It:	1) Select a weight which allows you to perform your target Training Zone in a safe and controlled manner.
	2) Now lie down onto a flat bench, taking a narrow grip on the bar of approx 8-10 inches width, and hold the barbell at full arm extension at the top of the movement.
	3) Slowly lower the bar down to the mid-chest line keeping the arms close to the sides of the body as you breathe in.
	4) Press the bar back out to the top of the movement whilst you breathe out and extend the arms.

Start Position:

Finish Position:

DIP AND CHIN ASSISTED MACHINE

THE SCIENCE

Muscles used:	(Dipping Movement).
Primarily:	The Tricep arm muscles (Long, Lateral,and Medial Heads).
Secondary:	The front and side shoulder (Anterior and Lateral Deltoid) muscles, forearm and Anconeus muscles, incorporating the lower portions of the Pectorals if leaning forward.
The Result:	Generally an all-round strength and mass-building exercise for the Triceps.
Who Is It For? Men + Women:	Wishing to increase their pressing power and/or build larger Triceps, or for specialist training purposes.
The Training Zone:	Strength: 3 sets of 10 reps. Bodybuilding: 4-6 sets of 8-12 reps.

THE ACTION

How To Do It:	1) Select a weight which allows you enough help to perform the movement.
	2) Decrease this weight as your strength increases over the following weeks.
	3) With your arms fully extended, place your feet/knees (dependent upon machine design) onto the relevant pads.
	4) Whilst bending your elbows until your arms are at 90°, breathe in allowing the counter-balance weight to go down.
	5) Now press out from this position whilst breathing out, allowing the counter-balance to assist you in returning to the starting position.

Start Position:

Finish Position:

LYING FRENCH PRESS

THE SCIENCE

Muscles used:	
Primary:	The Tricep arm (Long and Medial Head) muscles.
Secondary:	The Tricep (Lateral Head) muscles, forearm and Anconeus muscles in conjunction with to a lesser degree, the front shoulder (Anterior Deltoid) and Pectoral chest muscles.
The Result:	A mass-building and shaping exercise for the Tricep muscles.
Who Is It For? Men + Women:	Involved in bodybuilding exercise programmes.
The Training Zone:	Bodybuilding: 4-6 sets of 8-12 reps.

THE ACTION

How To Do It:	1) Select a weight which allows you to perform your target Training Zone in a safe and controlled manner.
	2) Now lie down onto a flat bench, taking a narrow grip onto a barbell or the centre camber of an EZ bar and hold it at full arm extension at the top of the movement.
	3) Now bend the elbows to allow the forearms to lower the bar down towards your forehead with the bar finishing either in line with your nose or behind the top of your head as you breathe in. (Personal comfort will dictate the finishing position of the bar).
	4) Ensure that the upper arms remain vertical with the elbows pointing towards the ceiling to gain the maximum stretch onto the Tricep muscles.
	5) Press the bar back out to the top of the movement whilst you breathe out and extend the arms.
NOTE WELL:	**Take care NOT TO JAR YOUR ELBOWS at the top of the movement.**

Start Position:

Finish Position:

LYING CABLE TRICEP EXTENSIONS

THE SCIENCE	
Muscles used:	
Primary:	The Tricep arm (Long and Medial Head) muscles.
Secondary:	The Tricep arm (Lateral Head) muscles, forearm and Anconeus muscles in conjunction with to a lesser degree, the front shoulder (Anterior Deltoid) and Pectoral chest muscles.
The Result:	A mass-building and shaping exercise for the Tricep muscles.
Who Is It For? Men + Women:	Requiring a more technically advanced exercise for the Tricep muscles, involved in bodybuilding exercise programmes.
The Training Zone:	Bodybuilding: 4-6 sets of 8-12 reps.
THE ACTION	
How To Do It:	1) Select a weight which allows you to perform your target Training Zone in a safe and controlled manner.
	2) Select either an EZ style or straight bar to clip onto the low pulley cable.
	3) Place a flat or low incline bench approximately 1-2 feet from the pulley.
	4) Using an overhand narrow grip, now lie down onto the bench with your back onto the support pad.
	5) Begin with your arms fully extended over your upper chest and throat region.
	6) Now bend the elbows to allow the forearms to lower the bar down towards your forehead with the bar finishing either in line with your nose or behind the top of your head as you breathe in. (Personal comfort will dictate the finishing position of the bar).
	7) Now slowly extend the arms back out towards the top of the starting position, whilst breathing out.
NOTE WELL:	**Take care NOT TO JAR YOUR ELBOWS at the top of the movement.**

Start Position:

Finish Position:

OVERHEAD CABLE TRICEP EXTENSIONS

	THE SCIENCE
Muscles used:	
Primary:	The Tricep arm (Long and Medial Head) muscles.
Secondary:	The Tricep (Lateral Head) muscles, forearm and Anconeus muscles in conjunction with to a lesser degree, the front shoulder (Anterior Deltoid) and Pectoral chest muscles.
The Result:	A mass-building and shaping exercise for the Tricep muscles.
Who Is It For? Men + Women:	Requiring a more technically advanced exercise for the Tricep muscles, involved in bodybuilding exercise programmes.
The Training Zone:	Bodybuilding: 4-6 sets of 8-12 reps.

	THE ACTION
How To Do It:	1) Select a weight which allows you to perform your target Training Zone in a safe and controlled manner.
	2) Select either an EZ style or straight bar to clip onto the high cable pulley.
	3) Using an overhead grip in line with your shoulders, keeping the bar above the head, take a stride forward, placing one foot in front of the other.
	4) Now bend your trunk forward to allow you to fully extend your arms without the cable touching your head whilst breathing out.
	5) Maintain the upper arms parallel with the floor as you bend your elbows and allow your hands to go back behind your head as you breathe in.

Start Position:

Finish Position:

SINGLE ARM DUMBELL TRICEP EXTENSIONS

THE SCIENCE	
Muscles used:	
Primary:	The Tricep arm (Long Head) muscles in conjunction with the Medial Head.
Secondary:	The Tricep arm (Lateral Head) muscles, and to a lesser degree the forearm and Anconeus muscles.
The Result:	An isolation exercise for shaping the Tricep arm muscles.
Who is it for?: Men + Women:	Involved in muscle toning and/or bodybuilding exercise programmes.
The Training Zone:	Muscle Tone: 2-3 sets of 12-15 reps. Bodybuilding: 4-6 sets of 8-12 reps.

THE ACTION	
How To Do It:	1) Select a weight which allows you to perform your target Training Zone in a safe and controlled manner.
	2) Sit on a bench with a back support and your feet placed firmly on the floor. Now, with your back flat against the padding, fully extend one arm above you, holding the dumbell with your palm facing forwards.
	3) Place your free hand for support on your upper arm and now bend your elbow whilst breathing in and allowing your forearm to come down behind the back of your neck, taking care NOT TO HIT THE BACK OF YOUR HEAD with the dumbell plates.
	4) Ensure your forearm goes down as deep as comfortable to gain the maximum stretch of the Tricep muscles before returning back to the starting position by fully extending the arm as you breathe out.

Start Position:

Finish Position:

LYING SINGLE ARM DUMBELL
TRICEP EXTENSIONS

THE SCIENCE

Muscles used:	
Primary:	The Tricep arm (Long and Medial Head) muscles, in conjunction with to a lesser degree the Lateral Head.
Secondary:	The forearm muscles, the Anconeus and front shoulder (Anterior Deltoid) muscles.
The Result:	An isolation exercise for shaping the Tricep arm muscles.
Who is it for?: Men + Women:	Involved in muscle toning and/or bodybuilding exercise programmes.
The Training Zone:	Muscle Tone: 2-3 sets of 12-15 reps. Bodybuilding: 4-6 sets of 8-12 reps.

THE ACTION

How To Do It:	1) Select a weight which allows you to perform your target Training Zone in a safe and controlled manner. 2) Lying down on a flat bench with the feet placed firmly on the floor, fully extend one arm above you holding the dumbell with your palm facing inwards towards the centre of your body. 3) Bend your elbow whilst breathing in and allow your forearm to come back down towards your Bicep muscles with the dumbell finishing at a point behind your shoulder region and if possible making contact with the bench. At this point your upper arm should be vertical with your elbow pointing to the ceiling. 4) Slowly extend the arm back out to it's starting position as you breathe out, using your other hand to support the upper arm at the correct angle throughout the entire movement.

Start Position:

Finish Position:

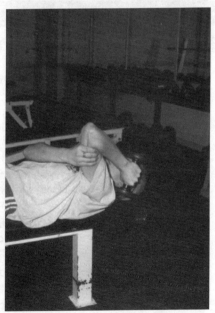

SINGLE ARM HORIZONTAL CABLE EXTENSIONS

THE SCIENCE	
Muscles used:	
Primary:	The Tricep arm (Long and Medial Head) muscles in conjunction with the Lateral Head to a lesser degree.
Secondary:	The forearm muscles, the shoulder muscles (Deltoids) and the Anconeus muscles.
The Result:	An isolation exercise which is primarily used for shaping the Triceps but also incorporated into bodybuilding programmes.
Who is it for?: Men + Women:	Involved in muscle toning and/or bodybuilding exercise programmes.
The Training Zone:	Muscle Tone: 2-3 sets of 12-15 reps. Bodybuilding: 4-6 sets of 8-12 reps.

THE ACTION	
How To Do It:	1) Select a weight which allows you to perform your target Training Zone in a safe and controlled manner.
	2) Using a stirrup handle on the high pulley, take an underhand grip and face away from the pulley machine.
	3) With the upper arm parallel to the ground, now extend out the forearm fully whilst breathing out, fully contracting the Triceps. Take care not to jar the elbow at the point of full extension.
	4) Bend the elbow to return the forearm back towards the Biceps and the palm of the hand close above the shoulder whilst breathing in.
	5) Maintain a good posture at all times with a flat back, and the opposite leg (in a "forward stride" position) to the arm being worked, throughout the entire movement.
	6) Ensure the feet of both the forward and reverse legs are flat on the foor surface at all times.
NOTE WELL:	DO NOT JAR THE ELBOWS WHEN EXTENDING THE ARM.

Start Position:

Finish Position:

SINGLE ARM CABLE TRICEP EXTENSIONS

THE SCIENCE

Muscles used:	
Primary:	The Tricep arm (Medial, Long and Lateral Head) muscles.
Secondary:	The forearm and Anconeus muscles.
The Result:	An isolation exercise placing emphasis on shaping the Tricep muscles.
Who is it for?: Men + Women:	Involved in bodybuilding exercise programmes.
The Training Zone:	Bodybuilding: 4-6 sets of 8-12 reps.

THE ACTION

How To Do It:	1) Select a weight which allows you to perform your target Training Zone in a safe and controlled manner.
	2) Place a stirrup handle onto the high cable pulley.
	3) Using an underhand grip with your palm facing your opposite chest side, stand upright keeping your back flat whilst you carefully fully extend the arm outwards and across your body whilst breathing out and finishing with your arm down the outside edge of your body.
	4) Slowly return back to the starting position, allowing your hand to come in and across your body whilst breathing in.

Start Position:

Finish Position:

SEATED INCLINE TRICEP EXTENSION MACHINE

THE SCIENCE

Muscles used:	
Primary:	The Tricep arm muscles (Long and Medial Heads).
Secondary:	The forearm muscles, the Anconeus muscles and the Tricep (Lateral Head) muscles, in conjunction with to a lesser degree, the front shoulder (Anterior Deltoid) and Pectoral chest muscles.
The Result:	A mass-building and shaping exercise for the Tricep muscles.
Who Is It For? Men + Women:	Involved in bodybuilding exercise programmes requiring a specialised movement to replace or supplement the Barbell Tricep Extensions (French Press) exercise.
The Training Zone:	Strength: 3 sets of 10 reps. Bodybuilding: 4-6 sets of 8-12 reps.

THE ACTION

How To Do It:	1) Select a weight which allows you to perform your target Training Zone in a safe and controlled manner.
	2) When seated ensure that your back is flat against the support pad.
	3) Press the foot lever forward to raise the narrow-grip handle up behind your head.
	4) Take a firm grip on the central curves of the handle, taking the strain onto the arms which should then be fully extended, whilst releasing the foot lever.
	5) With both feet flat on the ground, now slowly lower your hands down behind your head by bending your elbows whilst breathing in.
	6) Now breathe out and press out your hands to the top of the movement so that your arms are again fully extended.

Start Position:

Finish Position:

SEATED FRENCH PRESS

THE SCIENCE	
Muscles used:	
Primary:	The Tricep arm (Long and Medial Head) muscles.
Secondary:	The forearm muscles, the Anconeus muscles and the Tricep (Lateral Head) muscles, in conjunction with to a lesser degree, the front shoulder (Anterior Deltoid) muscles.
The Result:	A mass-building and shaping exercise for the Tricep muscles.
Who Is It For? Men + Women:	Involved in bodybuilding exercise programmes.
The Training Zone:	Strength:　　　3 sets of 10 reps. Bodybuilding: 4-6 sets of 8-12 reps.
THE ACTION	
How To Do It:	1) Select a weight which allows you to perform your target Training Zone in a safe and controlled manner. 2) Now sit down onto a bench with a back support, taking a narrow grip onto the centre camber of an EZ bar, and hold it at full arm extension at the top of the movement. 3) Now bend the elbows to allow the forearms to lower the bar down behind your head as you breathe in. 4) Ensure that the upper arms remain pointing forward to avoid allowing the elbows to flare outwards to the side. 5) Press the bar back out to the top of the movement whilst you breathe out and extend the arms.
NOTE WELL:	**Take care NOT TO JAR YOUR ELBOWS at the top of the movement.**

Start Position:

Finish Position:

REVERSE PUSHDOWNS

Muscles used:	
Primary:	The Tricep arm muscles (Lateral and Long Heads) in conjunction with the Medial Head to a lesser degree.
Secondary:	The forearm and Anconeus muscles, with to a lesser degree the shoulder (Deltoid) muscles.
The Result:	An exercise which is primarily used for shaping the Triceps but is also incorporated into bodybuilding programmes.
Who is it for?: Men + Women:	Primarily involved in bodybuilding exercise programmes.
The Training Zone:	Muscle Tone: 2-3 sets of 12-15 reps. Bodybuilding: 4-6 sets of 8-12 reps.

THE ACTION

How To Do It:	1) Select a weight which allows you to perform your target Training Zone in a safe and controlled manner.
	2) Take an underhand grip with the hands approximately in line with the front shoulders.
	3) Ensure your arms remain tucked in to the sides of your body whilst you push the weight down until your arms are fully extended to contract the Triceps whilst breathing out.
	4) Now bend your elbows and allow your forearms to come up a little past parallel to the floor whilst breathing in.
	5) Ensure you remain upright with a flat back through the entire movement.

Start Position:

Finish Position:

PRIMARY & SECONDARY MUSCLES

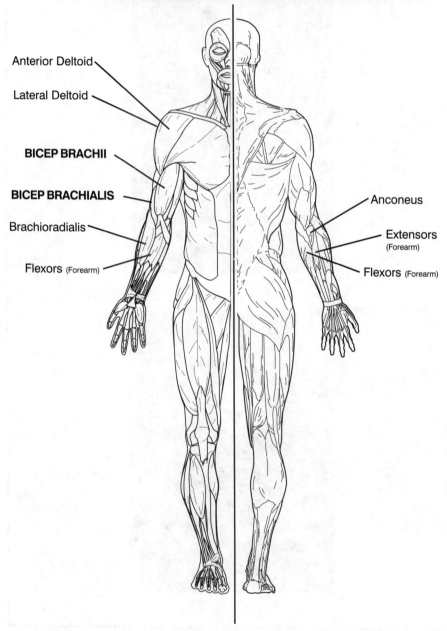

Anterior Deltoid

Lateral Deltoid

BICEP BRACHII

BICEP BRACHIALIS

Brachioradialis

Flexors (Forearm)

Anconeus

Extensors (Forearm)

Flexors (Forearm)

BICEP
EXERCISES

BICEP CURL MACHINE

THE SCIENCE

Muscles used:	
Primary:	The Bicep arm (Brachii and Brachialis) muscles.
Secondary:	The inner forearm (Flexor) muscles, Brachioradialis, and to a lesser degree the front and side shoulder (Anterior and Lateral Deltoid) muscles.
The Result:	Generally an all-round strength or mass-building exercise for the Biceps.
Who Is It For? Men + Women:	An exercise requiring minimal technical ability, suitable for general and specialist trainers involved in strength building and bodybuilding exercise programmes.
The Training Zone:	Muscle Tone: 2-3 sets of 12-15 reps. Strength: 3 sets of 10 reps. Bodybuilding: 4-6 sets of 8-12 reps.

THE ACTION

How To Do It:	1) Select a weight which allows you to perform your target Training Zone in a safe and controlled manner.
	2) Adjust the seat height so that your elbows are in line with the pivot point of the machine arm.
	3) Lean forward and grasp the handles firmly with the elbows bent using an underhand grip.
	4) Now lean back against the back support pad whilst keeping the elbows bent.
	5) Breathe out whilst "curling" the palms of your hands towards your front shoulders.
	6) Slowly return the handles $3/4$ of the way back to the starting position whilst breathing in.

Start Position:

Finish Position:

BARBELL CURLS

THE SCIENCE	
Muscles used:	
Primary:	The Bicep arm (Brachii and Brachialis) muscles.
Secondary:	The inner forearm (Flexor) muscles, Brachioradialis and to a lesser degree the front and side shoulder (Anterior and Lateral Deltoid) muscles.
The Result:	Places emphasis on building the main belly of the Bicep (Brachii) muscles.
Who Is It For? Men & Women:	Involved in strength building and bodybuilding exercise programmes.
The Training Zone:	Strength: 3 sets of 10 reps. Bodybuilding: 4-6 sets of 8-12 reps.

THE ACTION	
How To Do It:	1) Select a weight which allows you to perform your target Training Zone in a safe and controlled manner.
	2) Take an underhand grip on the bar in line with your front shoulder width.
	3) Now stand up straight keeping your back flat allowing your arms to hang straight in front of you with the bar touching your thighs.
	4) Keeping your upper arms at the side of your body, raise your hands up until the palms of your hands come up towards your front shoulders whilst breathing out.
	5) Slowly return back down to the starting position whilst breathing in.

Start Position:

Finish Position:

DUMBELL SUPINATION CURLS

THE SCIENCE

Muscles used:	
Primary:	The Bicep arm (Brachii and Brachialis) muscles.
Secondary:	The inner forearm (Flexor) muscles, and Brachioradialis and to a lesser degree the front and side shoulder (Anterior and Lateral Deltoid) muscles.
The Result:	A curling movement which places an equal emphasis on both building and shaping the Bicep arm muscles.
Who is it for?: Men + Women:	Requiring an excellent all-round exercise for the Biceps.
The Training Zone:	Muscle Tone: 2-3 sets of 12-15 reps. Strength: 3 sets of 10 reps. Bodybuilding: 4-6 sets of 8-12 reps.

THE ACTION

How To Do It:	1) Select a weight which allows you to perform your target Training Zone in a safe and controlled manner.
	2) Keeping your upper arms by the side of your body, palms facing inwards, bend the elbows until the forearms are at 90° angles and parallel with the ground before twisting (supinating) your palms upright and finishing the movement with your arm(s) fully bent with the palms of your hands close to the front shoulder (Anterior Deltoid) muscles whilst breathing out.
	3) Slowly lower the arms back down to their original position whilst breathing in.

Start Position:

Finish Position:

DUMBELL HAMMER CURLS

Muscles used:	
Primary:	The Bicep arm (Brachialis) muscles.
Secondary:	The Bicep arm (Brachii) muscles in conjunction with the forearm (Brachioradialis and Flexor) muscles and to a lesser degree the forearm (Extensor) muscles and the Anconeus muscles.
The Result:	A movement designed to place greater work onto the front surface of the Biceps, primarily for more shaping of the Brachialis in conjunction with forearm development.
Who is it for?: Men + Women:	Involved in muscle toning, strength building and bodybuilding exercise programmes.
The Training Zone:	Muscle Tone: 2-3 sets of 12-15 reps. Strength: 3 sets of 10 reps. Bodybuilding: 4-6 sets of 8-12 reps.

THE ACTION

How To Do It:	1) Select a weight which allows you to perform your target Training Zone in a safe and controlled manner.
	2) Keeping your upper arms by the sides of your body, palms facing inwards, bend the elbows until the forearms come up past parallel to the ground to an angle of less than 90° whilst breathing out, allowing the elbows to now travel forwards past the sides of your body slightly enabling you to gain a full contraction of the arms by finishing with the dumbell plates coming up to the front shoulder.
	3) Slowly lower the arms back down to their original position whilst breathing in, ensuring that you do not twist the hands (supinate) during this particular movement.

Start Position:

Finish Position:

DUMBELL CONCENTRATION CURLS

THE SCIENCE

Muscles used:	
Primary:	The Bicep arm (Brachii and Brachialis) muscles.
Secondary:	The inner forearm (Flexor) muscles, Brachioradialis, and to a lesser degree the front and side shoulder (Anterior and Lateral Deltoid) muscles.
The Result:	A curling movement which can be utilised to either place major emphasis on the shaping or the building of the Biceps dependent upon the technique used.
Who is it for?: Men + Women:	Involved in muscle toning and/or bodybuilding exercise programmes.
The Training Zone:	Muscle Tone: 2-3 sets of 12-15 reps. Bodybuilding: 4-6 sets of 8-12 reps.

THE ACTION

How To Do It:	1) Select a weight which allows you to perform your target Training Zone in a safe and controlled manner.
	2) Sit on the edge of a flat bench with your feet placed wider than your shoulder width on the floor.
	3) Place one hand onto the top of your thigh for support and stability, whilst taking hold of the dumbell in your other hand located along the inside line of your foot.
	4) With the back of your upper arm (Triceps) supported on the inside of your knee area, and the forearm running down the inside of your calf, now bend your elbow and curl the weight up to the top of the movement (your chest) whilst breathing out. Lower the weight back down to the starting position whilst breathing in.
	5) If you bring the dumbell to the same shoulder, you will develop increased mass and strength in the Bicep, or by taking the dumbell across to the opposite chest muscle area you will place a greater emphasis on shaping the Biceps.

Start Position 1:

Finish Position 1:

Start Position 2:

Finish Position 2:

EZ BAR CURLS

THE SCIENCE

Muscles used:	
Primary:	The Bicep arm (Brachii and Brachialis) muscles.
Secondary:	The inner forearm (Flexor) muscles, Brachioradialis, and to a lesser degree the front and side shoulder (Anterior and Lateral Deltoid) muscles.
The Result:	A curling movement which places emphasis on both building and shaping the Bicep arm muscles.
Who Is It For? Men & Women:	Involved in bodybuilding exercise programmes.
The Training Zone:	Bodybuilding: 4-6 sets of 8-12 reps.

THE ACTION

How To Do It:	1) Select a weight which allows you to perform your target Training Zone in a safe and controlled manner.
	2) Take an underhand grip on the angles of the bar in line with your front shoulders.
	3) Now stand up straight keeping your back flat allowing your arms to hang straight in front of you with the bar touching your thighs.
	4) Keeping your upper arms at the side of your body, curl your hands up until the palms of your hands come up to your shoulders whilst breathing out.
	5) Slowly return back down to the starting position whilst breathing in.
	6) By adapting a close grip on the central camber of the bar, you will throw the work outwards towards the outer regions of the Brachialis part of the Bicep group.

Start Position:

Finish Position:

PREACHER CURLS

Muscles used:	
Primary:	The Bicep arm (Brachii and Brachialis) muscles.
Secondary:	The inner forearm (Flexor) muscles, Brachioradialis, and to a lesser degree the front and side shoulder (Anterior and Lateral Deltoid) muscles.
The Result:	A superior style of curling, which can either; a) place emphasis on building & shaping the upper arm with an EZ style bar. OR: b) place emphasis on building the main belly of the Bicep (Brachii) with a straight bar.
Who Is It For? Men & Women:	Involved in bodybuilding exercise programmes.
The Training Zone:	Bodybuilding: 4-6 sets of 8-12 reps.

THE ACTION

How To Do It:	1) Select a weight which allows you to perform your target Training Zone in a safe and controlled manner.
	2) Select either an EZ style or straight bar, before sitting onto the preacher bench stool or seat.
	3) Using an underhand grip, slightly narrower than your shoulder width, whilst seated with your chest pressed against the pad, curl your hands up towards your front shoulders whilst breathing out.
	4) Slowly return back down towards the starting position whilst breathing in, and ensuring that your arms remain in contact with the support pad throughout the entire movement.
NOTE WELL:	Ensure when lowering the bar downwards, you only extend the arms $3/4$ of the way to fully straight - this will stop you from hyper-extending your arm, which could result in damage to your elbows.

Start Position:

Finish Position:

CABLE CURLS

Muscles used:	
Primary:	The Bicep arm (Brachii and Brachialis) muscles.
Secondary:	The inner forearm (Flexor) muscles, Brachioradialis, and to a lesser degree the front and side shoulder (Anterior and Lateral Deltoid) muscles.
The Result:	A version of curling, which can either; a) place emphasis on building & shaping the upper arm with an EZ style bar. *OR:* b) place emphasis on building the main belly of the Bicep (Brachii) with a straight bar.
Who Is It For? Men + Women:	Requiring an exercise for the development of the main belly of the Bicep (Brachii), particularly at the lower end near the elbow crease (Bicipital Apponeurosis). Sometimes used by fitness trainers in gymnasiums with limited Bicep training facilities.
The Training Zone:	Muscle Tone: 2-3 sets of 12-15 reps. Bodybuilding: 4-6 sets of 8-12 reps.

THE ACTION

How To Do It:	1) Select a weight which allows you to perform your target Training Zone in a safe and controlled manner.
	2) Select either an EZ style or straight bar to clip onto the low pulley cable.
	3) Now stand up straight keeping your back flat allowing your arms to hang straight in front of you with the bar touching your thighs.
	4) Keeping your upper arms at the side of your body, curl the bar up until the palms of your hands come up towards your front shoulders whilst breathing out.
	5) Slowly return back down to the starting position whilst breathing in.
	6) Using an EZ style bar will increase the amount of work put onto the Brachialis part of the Bicep group.

Start Position:

Finish Position:

CABLE PREACHER CURLS

THE SCIENCE

Muscles used:	
Primary:	The Bicep arm (Brachii and Brachialis) muscles.
Secondary:	The inner forearm (Flexor) muscles, Brachioradialis and to a lesser degree the front and side shoulder (Anterior and Lateral Deltoid) muscles.
The Result:	A superior version of 'preacher' style curling, which can either; a) place emphasis on building & shaping the upper arm with an EZ style bar. *OR:* b) place emphasis on building the main belly of the Bicep (Brachii) with a straight bar.
Who Is It For? Men + Women:	Requiring an excellent exercise for bodybuilding training done in a strict style.
The Training Zone:	Bodybuilding: 4-6 sets of 8-12 reps.

THE ACTION

How To Do It:	1) Select a weight which allows you to perform your target Training Zone in a safe and controlled manner.
	2) Select either an EZ style or straight bar to clip onto the low pulley cable.
	3) Place a Preacher bench approximately 1-2 feet from the pulley.
	4) Using a underhand grip, slightly narrower than your shoulder width, whilst seated with your chest pressed against the pad, curl your hands up towards your front shoulders whilst breathing out.
	5) Slowly return back down towards the starting position whilst breathing in, and ensuring that your arms remain in contact with the support pad throughout the entire movement.
NOTE WELL:	**Ensure when lowering the bar downwards, you only extend the arms $^3/_4$ of the way to fully straight - this will stop you from hyper-extending your arm, which could result in damage to your elbows.**

Start Position:

Finish Position:

SINGLE ARM CABLE CONCENTRATION CURLS

	THE SCIENCE
Muscles used:	
Primary:	The Bicep arm (Brachialis) muscles.
Secondary:	The Bicep arm (Brachii) muscles, the inner forearm (Flexor) muscles together with the Brachioradialis and to a lesser degree the front and side shoulder (Anterior and Lateral Deltoid) muscles.
The Result:	This exercise places emphasis on shaping and peaking the Biceps group, concentrating on one arm at a time.
Who Is It For? Men + Women:	Requiring a more technically advanced exercise for shaping the Bicep muscles, which can be enhanced by the use of a Preacher bench.
The Training Zone:	Bodybuilding: 4-6 sets of 8-12 reps.
	THE ACTION
How To Do It:	1) Select a weight which allows you to perform your target Training Zone in a safe and controlled manner.
	2) Place a stirrup handle onto the low pulley cable.
	3) Using an underhand grip stand up keeping your back flat and your arm fully extended and the Bicep positioned close into the outer chest region or flat against the pad of a Preacher bench.
	4) From this position, curl the palm of your hand across your body until it comes to the opposite front shoulder whilst breathing out.
	5) Slowly return back down and across to the starting position whilst breathing in.

Start Position:

Finish Position:

SINGLE ARM CABLE CONCENTRATION CURLS

THE SCIENCE

Muscles used:	
Primary:	The Bicep arm (Brachii) muscles.
Secondary:	The Bicep arm (Brachialis) muscles and inner forearm (Flexor) muscles together with the Brachioradialis and to a lesser degree the front and side shoulder (Anterior and Lateral Deltoid) muscles.
The Result:	This exercise places emphasis on building the main belly of the Bicep, concentrating on one arm at a time.
Who Is It For? Men + Women:	Requiring an exercise for bodybuilding training done in a strict style which can be enhanced by the use of a Preacher bench.
The Training Zone:	Bodybuilding: 4-6 sets of 8-12 reps.

THE ACTION

How To Do It:	1) Select a weight which allows you to perform your target Training Zone in a safe and controlled manner.
	2) Place a stirrup handle onto the low pulley cable.
	3) Using an underhand grip, stand up keeping your back flat and ensure that the upper arm being worked remains rigid against the side of your body or against the pad of a Preacher bench.
	4) Now curl the palm of your hand up until it comes close to your front shoulder whilst breathing out.
	5) Slowly return back down to the starting position whilst breathing in.
NOTE WELL:	**Ensure when lowering the handle downwards, you only extend the arms $3/4$ of the way to fully straight - this will stop you from hyper-extending your arm, which could result in damage to your elbows.**

Start Position:

Finish Position:

PRIMARY & SECONDARY MUSCLES

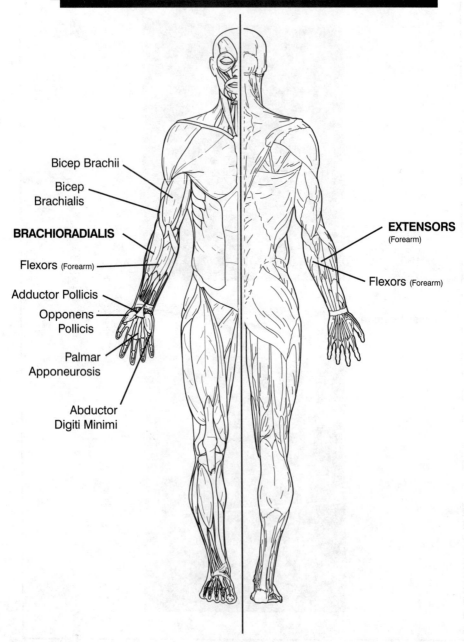

Bicep Brachii

Bicep Brachialis

BRACHIORADIALIS

Flexors (Forearm)

Adductor Pollicis

Opponens Pollicis

Palmar Apponeurosis

Abductor Digiti Minimi

EXTENSORS (Forearm)

Flexors (Forearm)

FOREARM
EXERCISES

DUMBELL WRIST CURLS

THE SCIENCE

Muscles used:	
Primary:	The forearm (Flexor) muscles.
Secondary:	The forearm (Extensor) muscles in conjunction with the Opponens Pollicis, Adductor Pollicis, Abductor Digiti Minimi and Palmar Apponeurosis muscles of the hand.
The Result:	Builds an increased grip strength and inner forearm muscular development.
Who Is It For? Men & Women:	Involved in sports specific, strength building and bodybuilding exercise programmes.
The Training Zone:	Strength: 3 sets of 10 reps. Bodybuilding: 4-6 sets of 8-12 reps.

THE ACTION

How To Do It:	1) Select a weight which allows you to perform your target Training Zone in a safe and controlled manner.
	2) Sit down on the edge of a flat bench with your thighs parallel to the floor, allowing you to rest the back of your forearm along the top of your thigh whilst holding a dumbell with an underhand grip. Use your opposite arm to stabilize your elbow by placing your hand on your forearm.
	3) Ensure that the back of your hand can now stretch down to touch the front surface of your knee without your elbow lifting off your thigh as you breathe in.
	4) Slowly curl your hand upwards contracting your inner forearm muscles as you breathe out.
	5) Slowly return back to the starting position whilst breathing in.

Start Position:

Finish Position:

BARBELL WRIST CURLS

THE SCIENCE

Muscles used:	
Primary:	The forearm (Flexor) muscles.
Secondary:	The forearm (Extensor) muscles in conjunction with the Opponens Pollicis, Abductor Pollicis, Abductor Digiti Minimi and Palmar Apponeurosis muscles of the hand.
The Result:	Builds an increased grip strength and inner forearm muscular development.
Who Is It For? Men & Women:	Involved in sports specific, strength building and bodybuilding exercise programmes.
The Training Zone:	Strength: 3 sets of 10 reps. Bodybuilding: 4-6 sets of 8-12 reps.

THE ACTION

How To Do It:	1) Select a weight which allows you to perform your target Training Zone in a safe and controlled manner.
	2) Sit down on the edge of a flat bench with your thighs parallel to the floor, allowing you to rest the backs of your forearms along the tops of your thighs whilst holding a barbell with an underhand grip with the hands shoulder width apart.
	3) Ensure that the backs of your hands can now stretch down to touch the front surface of your knees without your elbows lifting off your thighs as you breathe in.
	4) Slowly curl your hands upwards contracting your inner forearm muscles as you breathe out.
	5) Slowly return back to the starting position whilst breathing in.

Start Position:

Finish Position:

REVERSE CABLE CURLS

THE SCIENCE

Muscles used:	
Primary:	The outer forearm muscles (Extensors and Brachioradialis) and the Brachialis part of the Bicep Group.
Secondary:	The inner forearm muscles (Flexors) and partially the Brachii part of the Bicep group.
The Result:	Builds grip strength and overall development of the Brachioradialis and Extensor forearm muscles whilst taxing the outer part of the Bicep arm group (Brachialis).
Who Is It For? Men + Women:	Involved in sports specific strength building and bodybuilding exercise programmes.
The Training Zone:	Strength: 3 sets of 10 reps. Bodybuilding: 4-6 sets of 8-12 reps.

THE ACTION

How To Do It	1) Select a weight which allows you to perform your target Training Zone in a safe and controlled manner.
	2) Place a straight bar onto the low pulley cable and take an overhand grip in line with your front shoulder width.
	3) Now stand up straight keeping your back flat allowing your arms to hang straight in front of you with the bar touching your thighs.
	4) Keeping your upper arms at the side of your body, curl your hands up until the backs of your hands come up close to your front shoulders whilst breathing out.
	5) Slowly return back down towards the starting position whilst breathing in.
	6) Using an EZ style bar will put more of the stress onto the Brachioradialis part of the forearm and less stress onto the wrists.

Start Position:

Finish Position:

REVERSE BARBELL CURLS

THE SCIENCE

Muscles used:	
Primary:	The outer forearm muscles (Extensors and Brachioradialis) and the Brachialis part of the Bicep Group.
Secondary:	The inner forearm muscles (Flexors) and partially the Brachii part of the Bicep group.
The Result:	Builds grip strength and overall development of the Brachioradialis and Extensor forearm muscles whilst taxing the outer part of the Bicep arm group (Brachialis).
Who Is It For? Men + Women:	Involved in sports specific strength building and bodybuilding exercise programmes.
The Training Zone:	Strength: 3 sets of 10 reps. Bodybuilding: 4-6 sets of 8-12 reps.

THE ACTION

How To Do It:	1) Select a weight which allows you to perform your target Training Zone in a safe and controlled manner.
	2) Take an overhand grip on the barbell in line with your front shoulder width.
	3) Now stand up straight keeping your back flat allowing your arms to hang straight in front of you with the bar touching your thighs.
	4) Keeping your upper arms at the side of your body, curl your hands up until the back of your hands come up close to your front shoulders whilst breathing out.
	5) Slowly return back down towards the starting position whilst breathing in.
	6) Using an EZ style bar will put more of the stress onto the Brachioradialis part of the forearm and less stress onto the wrists.

Start Position:

Finish Position:

PRIMARY & SECONDARY MUSCLES

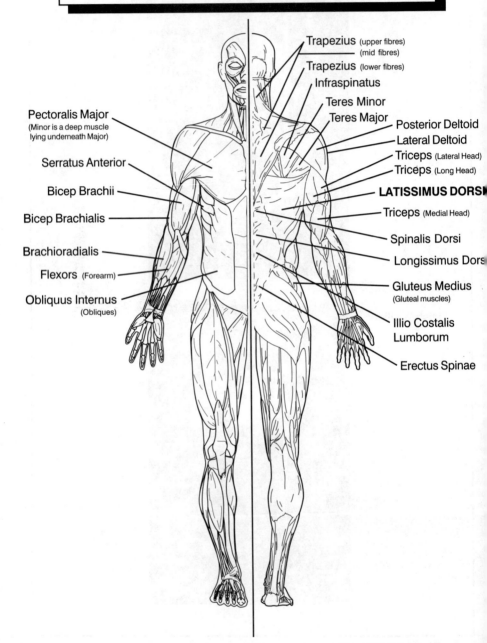

Trapezius (upper fibres)
(mid fibres)
Trapezius (lower fibres)
Infraspinatus
Teres Minor
Teres Major
Posterior Deltoid
Lateral Deltoid
Triceps (Lateral Head)
Triceps (Long Head)
LATISSIMUS DORSI
Triceps (Medial Head)
Spinalis Dorsi
Longissimus Dorsi
Gluteus Medius
(Gluteal muscles)
Illio Costalis
Lumborum
Erectus Spinae

Pectoralis Major
(Minor is a deep muscle
lying underneath Major)

Serratus Anterior

Bicep Brachii

Bicep Brachialis

Brachioradialis

Flexors (Forearm)

Obliquus Internus
(Obliques)

BACK
EXERCISES

LATERAL PULLDOWNS

THE SCIENCE

Muscles used:	
Primary:	The major back muscles (Latissimus Dorsi) in conjunction with the Trapezius neck muscles (lower fibres).
Secondary:	The Bicep arm (Brachii and Brachialis) muscles, the forearm (Brachioradialis and Flexor) muscles, Teres Major and Minor, Infraspinatus and rear shoulder (Posterior Deltoid) muscles.
The Result:	An exercise providing excellent shaping of the back whilst pulling down behind the neck, whilst also providing additional building capabilities when pulling down to the chest (advanced version).
Who is it for?: Men + Women:	Involved in general fitness and/or bodybuilding programmes.
The Training Zone:	Muscle Tone: 2-3 sets of 12-15 reps. Endurance: 3 sets of 15-25 reps or 25-50 reps Elite level. Strength: 3 sets of 10 reps. Bodybuilding: 4-6 sets of 8-12 reps.

THE ACTION

How To Do It:	1) Select a weight which allows you to perform your target Training Zone in a safe and controlled manner.
	2) Take a wide grip approximately 8-10 inches past shoulder width for pulling down behind the neck and a grip width just past your shoulders for pulldowns to the front.
	3) Behind the neck pulldowns should be done whilst breathing out on the effort, but with front pulldowns - breathing in as the bar comes to the chest will assist you in obtaining a more superior contraction.
	4) Ensure the arms are fully extended to stretch the back at the top of the movement, and that you obtain a strict controlled muscle contraction in the back as you pull the bar down to a finishing position.

Start Position 1:

Finish Position 1:

Start Position 2:

Finish Position 2:

CLOSE-GRIP PULLDOWNS

THE SCIENCE

Muscles used:	
Primary:	The major back muscles (Latissimus Dorsi), in conjunction with the Trapezius neck muscles (mid to upper fibres).
Secondary:	The Bicep arm (Brachii and Brachialis) muscles, the forearm (Brachioradialis and Flexor) muscles, Teres Major and Minor, Infraspinatus and rear shoulder (Posterior Deltoid) muscles.
The Result:	An exercise for building the upper back which can also provide some shaping of the Latissimus muscles.
Who is it for?: Men + Women:	Involved in strength building and bodybuilding exercise programmes.
The Training Zone:	Strength: 3 sets of 10 reps. Bodybuilding: 4-6 sets of 8-12 reps.

THE ACTION

How To Do It:	1) Select a weight which allows you to perform your target Training Zone in a safe and controlled manner. 2) Grasp the close-grip handle with the palms of your hands facing each other, and your arms fully extended to stretch the back. 3) Now pull the handle down to the mid-chest line as you throw the chest forward and shoulders back to create a maximum contraction onto the Latissimus muscles as you breathe in. 4) Continue looking up at the cable pulley whilst you extend the arms back out to the top of the movement, stretching the back, and breathing out.

Start Position:

Finish Position:

I.B.S. HIGH ROW

THE SCIENCE

Muscles used:	
Primary:	The major back muscles (Latissimus Dorsi), in conjunction with the Trapezius neck muscles (mid to upper fibres).
Secondary:	The Bicep arm (Brachii and Brachialis) muscles, the forearm (Brachioradialis and Flexor) muscles, Teres Major and Minor, Infraspinatus and rear shoulder (Posterior Deltoid) muscles.
The Result:	An exercise for building the upper back which can also provide some shaping of the Latissimus muscles.
Who is it for?: Men + Women:	Involved in strength building and bodybuilding exercise programmes.
The Training Zone:	Strength: 3 sets of 10 reps. Bodybuilding: 4-6 sets of 8-12 reps.

THE ACTION

How To Do It:	1) Select a weight which allows you to perform your target Training Zone in a safe and controlled manner. 2) Adjust the seat and knee-pad heights so that you can reach the handles when your arms are fully extended. 3) Now pull the handles down to the mid-chest line as you throw the chest forward and shoulders back to create a maximum contraction onto the Latissimus muscles as you breathe in. 4) Continue looking up whilst you extend the arms back out to the top of the movement, stretching the back, and breathing out.

Start Position 1:

Finish Position 1:

Start Position 2:

Finish Position 2:

REVERSE GRIP PULLDOWNS

THE SCIENCE

Muscles used:	
Primary:	The major back muscles (Latissimus Dorsi) in conjunction with the Trapezius neck muscles.
Secondary:	The Bicep arm (Brachii and Brachialis) muscles, the forearm (Brachioradialis and Flexor) muscles, Teres Major and Minor, Infraspinatus and rear shoulder (Posterior Deltoid) muscles.
The Result:	An exercise for building the upper back which can also provide some shaping of the Latissimus muscles. A useful exercise when training to perform chin-ups.
Who is it for? Men + Women:	Involved in strength and bodybuilding programmes.
The Training Zone:	Strength: 3 sets of 10 reps. Bodybuilding: 4-6 sets of 8-12 reps.

THE ACTION

How To Do It:	1) Select a weight which allows you to perform your target Training Zone in a safe and controlled manner. 2) Take a grip on the Lateral Pulldown bar in line with your front shoulders with the palms of your hands facing towards you. 3) With the arms fully extended, stretching the back, pull the bar down to the mid-chest line as you throw the chest forward and shoulders back to create a maximum contraction onto the Latissimus muscles as you breathe in. 4) Continue looking up at the cable pulley whilst you extend the arms back out to the top of the movement, stretching the back, and breathing out.

Start Position:

Finish Position:

STRAIGHT ARM PULLDOWNS

THE SCIENCE

Muscles used:	
Primary:	The major back muscles (Latissimus Dorsi) in conjunction with the Trapezius neck muscles (mid to upper fibres).
Secondary:	Teres Major and Minor, Infraspinatus and rear shoulder (Posterior Deltoid) muscles, forearm (Brachioradialis and Flexor) muscles, Tricep arm muscles and the Serratus Anterior muscles in conjunction with the lower chest fibres to a lesser degree.
The Result:	A shaping exercise for the back which acts in a similar way to the Pullover machine, predominantly isolating the Latissimus muscles.
Who is it for?: Men + Women:	Involved in bodybuilding programmes.
The Training Zone:	Bodybuilding: 4-6 sets of 8-12 reps.

THE ACTION

How To Do It:	1) Select a weight which allows you to perform your target Training Zone in a safe and controlled manner.
	2) Take an overhand grip on a flat bar and step back from the high pulley so as to allow you to adopt a "semi-water skiing" stance, with the arms stretched out parallel to the ground in front of you.
	3) Now, whilst breathing in and keeping the knees slightly bent, pull the bar down in front of you to your thighs as you throw the shoulders back and the chest forward to arch the back and gain a superior contraction of the Latissimus muscles.
	4) Ensure that the arms remain fully extended as you raise the bar off the thighs and back to parallel with the ground in front of you as you breathe out and stretch the Latissimus muscles.

Start Position:

Finish Position:

DIP AND CHIN ASSISTED MACHINE

THE SCIENCE

Muscles used:	(Chinning Movement)
Primary:	The major back muscles (Latissimus Dorsi) in conjunction with the Trapezius neck muscles (lower fibres).
Secondary:	The Bicep arm (Brachialis and Brachii) muscles, the forearm (Brachioradialis and Flexor) muscles, Teres Major and Minor, Infraspinatus and rear shoulder (Posterior Deltoid) muscles.
The Result:	An exercise providing excellent width-building and shaping of the back whilst strengthening the arms.
Who Is It For? Men + Women:	Requiring greater back development, who are already accomplished at front Lateral Pulldowns and rowing movements.
The Training Zone:	Strength: 3 sets of 10 reps. Bodybuilding: 4-6 sets of 8-12 reps.

THE ACTION

How To Do It:	1) Select a weight which allows you enough help to perform the movement.
*	2) Decrease this weight as your strength increases over the following weeks. With no weight assistance you will now be performing the classical "Wide Grip Chins" as a free exercise.
	3) With your arms fully extended, place your feet/knees (dependent upon machine design) onto the relevant pads.
	4) Whilst bending your elbows until your chin comes up to the handle bars, breathe out allowing the counter-balance weight to go up.
	5) Now slowly lower yourself back to the starting position whilst breathing in to allow the counter-balance weight to go down.

Start Position:

Finish Position:

SEATED CABLE ROWS

THE SCIENCE

Muscles used:	
Primary:	The major back muscles (Latissimus Dorsi) in conjunction with the Trapezius neck muscles (mid to upper fibres).
Secondary:	The Bicep arm muscles (Brachii and Brachialis, the forearm (Brachioradialis and Flexor) muscles, and the lower back (Erectus Spinae) muscles, Teres Major and Minor, Infraspinatus and rear shoulder (Posterior Deltoid) muscles.
The Result:	An exercise for building and shaping the back : a) Close grip handles will provide more muscle thickness. b) Wide grip bars will provide more width and shape for the back.
Who Is It For? Men + Women:	Involved in strength building and bodybuilding exercise programmes.
The Training Zone:	Strength: 3 sets of 10 reps. Bodybuilding: 4-6 sets of 8-12 reps.

THE ACTION

How To Do It:	1) Select a weight which allows you to perform your target Training Zone in a safe and controlled manner.
	2) Place either the close grip handles or straight bar onto the lower pulley cable.
	3) Take an overhand grip on the wide bar at past shoulder width or a palms in grip on the close grip handles and place both feet securely on the footpegs provided as you sit down.
	4) Now sit upright with your knees slightly bent and lock them in this position. (Your arms at this stage should now be fully extended).
	5) Stretch forward to allow the handles or bar to reach your feet on the foot pegs as far as comfortable. (This will stretch the Latissimus muscles). Breathe out through this part of the movement.
	6) Now as you begin to sit upright again, pull the handles or bar in towards your lower abdomen and breathe in, to assist you in throwing the shoulders back and the chest forward to contract the Latissimus muscles.
	7) The finishing position will be when you are in an upright position with the hands close-in to the abdomen.

Start Position:

Finish Position:

SINGLE ARM DUMBELL ROW

THE SCIENCE

Muscles used:	
Primary:	The major back muscles (Latissimus Dorsi) in conjunction with the Trapezius neck muscles (when looking forward).
Secondary:	The Bicep arm (Brachii and Brachialis) muscles, the forearm (Brachioradialis and Flexor) muscles, Teres Major and Minor, Infraspinatus and rear shoulder (Posterior Deltoid) muscles.
The Result:	An exercise providing shaping of the back muscles when performed in a straight "sawing" action movement, or which can also incorporate additional building of the upper Latissimus muscle and the Teres Major when pronating the hand at the top of the movement.
Who is it for?: Men + Women:	Involved in general fitness and/or bodybuilding exercise programmes.
The Traing Zone:	Muscle Tone: 2-3 sets of 12-15 reps. Bodybuilding: 4-6 sets of 8-12 reps.

THE ACTION

How To Do It:	1) Select a weight which allows you to perform your target Training Zone in a safe and controlled manner.
	2) Begin by hooking the foot of one leg over the end of a flat bench when kneeling on it, and using the same side arm fully extended as a support at an angle which allows the back to be parallel to the ground, with the free leg spread away from the bench to create a wide base - now using your remaining free hand to pull the dumbell up to the outside edge of the chest whilst breathing in.
	3) Now as you breathe out, allow the arm to stretch back down towards the floor whilst holding the dumbell. To enable a full stretch and contraction of the back muscles on the side being worked, the torso will have to twist slightly at the top and bottom of the movements.

Start Position:

Finish Position:

SEATED T-BAR ROW MACHINE

THE SCIENCE

Muscles used:	
Primary:	The major back muscles (Latissimus Dorsi) in conjunction with the Trapezius neck muscles (mid to lower fibres).
Secondary:	The Bicep arm (Brachii and Brachialis) muscles, forearm (Brachioradialis and Flexor) muscles, and rear shoulder (Posterior Deltoid) muscles and the upper back muscles (Teres Major, Teres Minor, Infraspinatus).
The Result:	A general exercise providing upper back conditioning work without stressing the lower back (Erectus Spinae).
Who Is It For? Men + Women:	Requiring a back exercise which affords safety for a weak lower back.
The Training Zone:	Muscle Tone: 2-3 sets of 15-25 reps. Endurance: 3 sets of 15-25 reps. Strength: 3 sets of 10 reps.

THE ACTION

How To Do It:	1) Select a weight which allows you to perform your target Training Zone in a safe and controlled manner.
	2) Adjust the seat height so that when your arms are extended forward to grasp the handles, your arms are parallel to the ground.
	3) Ensure the chest pad is set to enable you to stretch your arms when returning the pivot arms to the starting position.
	4) Taking hold of the pivot arm handles, keep your back flat and your chest in contact with the front support pad and pull the handles in towards the sides of your lower chest whilst breathing out.
	5) Slowly return back to the starting position whilst breathing in.
	6) Place your feet comfortably onto the revelant foot pegs provided throughout the entire movement.

Start Position:

Finish Position:

SPIDER ROW MACHINE

Muscles used:	
Primary:	The major back muscles (Latissimus Dorsi) in conjuction with the Trapezius neck muscles.
Secondary:	The Bicep arm (Brachii and Brachialis) muscles forearm (Brachioradialis and Flexor) muscles, and rear shoulder (Posterior Deltoid) muscles and the upper back muscles (Teres Major, Teres Minor, Infraspinatus).
The Result:	An exercise providing excellent mass-building and shaping of the back whilst strengthening the arms without stressing the lower back (Erectus Spinae).
Who Is It For? Men + Women:	Involved in strength building and bodybuilding exercise programmes.
The Training Zone:	Strength: 3 sets of 10 reps. Bodybuilding: 4-6 sets of 8-12 reps.

THE ACTION

How To Do It:	1) Select a weight which allows you to perform your target Training Zone in a safe and controlled manner.
	2) Place your feet hip-width apart onto the training platform so that your chest rests comfortably onto the support pad.
	3) Select a medium width grip in line with the front shoulders and release the bar from its supporting rest pins.
	4) Now pull the bar up as far as possible until your hands are in line with the sides of your chest as you breathe in and look straight ahead.
	5) Now lower the bar back down until your arms are fully extended to stretch the back muscles as you breathe out.

Start Position:

Finish Position:

SINGLE ARM CABLE ROWS

THE SCIENCE

Muscles used:	
Primary:	The major back muscles (Latissimus Dorsi) and Teres Major in conjunction with the Trapezius neck muscles.
Secondary:	The rear shoulder (Posterior Deltoid) muscles, the Bicep arm (Brachialis) muscles, and forearm (Brachioradialis and Flexor) muscles.
The Result:	A specialist exercise for the development of the lower Latissimus muscles.
Who Is It For? Men + Women:	Requiring a more technical exercise for bodybuilding exercise programmes.
The Training Zone:	Bodybuilding: 4-6 sets of 8-12 reps.

THE ACTION

How To Do It:	1) Select a weight which allows you to perform your target Training Zone in a safe and controlled manner.
	2) Place a stirrup handle onto the low cable pulley cable and take a palm-in grip on the handle, with one hand as you sit down and place the foot of the opposite leg onto the foot-pegs provided. Alternatively, this exercise can be done from a standing position as shown in the photographs.
	3) Now sit upright with your knee slightly bent and lock your leg in this position. (Your arm at this stage should now be fully extended).
	4) Stretch forward to allow the handle to reach the foot-peg or as far forward as comfortable. (This will stretch the Latissimus muscle). Breathe out through this part of the movement as you turn the shoulder on the side being worked, into the movement and towards the pulley.
	5) Slowly turn the shoulder on the side of the body being worked away from the machine as you pull the handle back and into your waist whilst breathing in to contract the Latissimus muscles. By rotating the palm of the hand you can place additional emphasis onto the Teres Minor and Infraspinatus muscles also.

Start Position:

Finish Position:

I.B.S. ROW

THE SCIENCE

Muscles used:	
Primary:	The major back muscles (Latissimus Dorsi) in conjunction with the Trapezius neck muscles (mid to upper fibres).
Secondary:	The Bicep arm (Brachii and Brachialis) muscles, the forearm (Brachioradialis and Flexor) muscles and the lower back (Erectus Spinae) muscles, Teres Major and Minor, Infraspinatus and rear shoulder (Posterior Deltoid) muscles.
The Result:	A specialist exercise for the development of the lower Latissimus muscles.
Who Is It For? Men + Women:	Requiring a more technical exercise for bodybuilding exercise programmes.
The Training Zone:	Bodybuilding: 4-6 sets of 8-12 reps.

THE ACTION

How To Do It:	1) Select a weight which allows you to perform your target Training Zone in a safe and controlled manner.
	2) Adjust the seat and knee-pad heights so that you can reach the handles when your arms are fully extended.
	3) Now either pull one handle or both together back towards your side chest(s) breathing in as you contract the Latissimus muscles.
	4) Slowly return the handles or handle back to the starting position whilst breathing out and stretching the back.
	5) If training each side of the body alternatively, now repeat steps 3 and 4 on the opposite arm.

Start Position:

Finish Position:

KNEELING SINGLE ARM PULLDOWNS

THE SCIENCE

Muscles used:	
Primary:	The major back muscles (Latissimus Dorsi), in conjunction with the Trapezius neck muscles.
Secondary:	The Bicep arm (Brachii and Brachialis) muscles, the forearm muscles, Teres Major and Minor, Infraspinatus and rear shoulder (Posterior Deltoid) muscles.
The Result:	An exercise for shaping the Latissimus muscles.
Who is it for?: Men + Women:	Involved in bodybuilding exercise programmes.
The Training Zone:	Bodybuilding: 4-6 sets of 8-12 reps.

THE ACTION

How To Do It:	1) Select a weight which allows you to perform your target Training Zone in a safe and controlled manner.
	2) Grasp a stirrup handle on the high pulley with the palm facing inwards and with the arm fully extended stretching the back, kneel down approximately 2 feet away from the base of the machine (kneeling on the same side of the body as you are pulling down with).
	3) Keep your hips square to the cable machine as you execute the movement, allowing the shoulders to twist towards the machine as you stretch the Latissimus muscles.
	4) Pull the handle down and into the side of the body whilst breathing in, and continuing to look up at the cable pulley.
	5) Now return the arm back out to full extension whilst breathing out.

Start Position:

Finish Position:

T-BAR ROW

THE SCIENCE

Muscles used:	
Primary:	The major back muscles (Latissimus Dorsi) in conjuction with the Trapezius neck muscles.
Secondary:	The Bicep arm (Brachii and Brachialis) muscles, forearm (Brachioradialis and Flexor) muscles, rear shoulder (Posterior Deltoid) muscles, lower back (Erectus Spinae) muscles and upper back muscles (Teres Major, Teres Minor, Infraspinatus).
The Result:	An exercise providing excellent mass-building and shaping of the back whilst strengthening the arms.
Who Is It For? Men + Women:	Involved in strength building and bodybuilding exercise programmes.
The Training Zone:	Strength: 3 sets of 10 reps. Bodybuilding: 4-6 sets of 8-12 reps.

THE ACTION

How To Do It?	1) Select a weight which allows you to perform your target Training Zone in a safe and controlled manner.
	2) Place the feet hip-width apart on the training platform, bending the legs whilst taking a grip on the bar of less than shoulder width.
	3) Straighten the legs to approximately $^3/_4$ of the way allowing the arms to be fully extended with the weight hanging down as you look forwards.
	4) Now pull the T-bar up until your hands bring the bar in close to the abdominal region, ensuring the weight discs do not hit your chest at the top of the movement as you breathe in.
	5) Continue looking forward throughout the entire movement and NOT DOWN as you lower the weight back down and breathe out.
	6) Ensure you fully stretch the Latissimus muscles at the bottom of the movement, and throw the chest forward and shoulders back at the top of the movement to gain the maximum muscular contraction.
	7) Only undertake this exercise if your back is sound and free from injury.

Start Position:

Finish Position:

BARBELL BENT-OVER ROWS

	THE SCIENCE
Muscles used:	
Primary:	The major back muscles (Latissimus Dorsi) in conjuction with the Trapezius neck muscles.
Secondary:	The Bicep arm (Brachii and Brachialis) muscles, forearm (Brachioradialis and Flexor) muscles, rear shoulder (Posterior Deltoid) muscles, lower back (Erectus Spinae) muscles, and the back extensor (Spinalis Dorsi, Longissimus Dorsi & Illio Costalis Lumborum) muscles.
The Result:	An exercise providing excellent mass-building and shaping of the back whilst strengthening the arms.
Who Is It For? Men + Women:	Involved in strength building and bodybuilding exercise programmes.
The Training Zone:	Strength: 3 sets of 10 reps. Bodybuilding:4-6 sets of 8-12 reps.

	THE ACTION
How to Do It:	1) Select a weight which allows you to perform your target Training Zone in a safe and controlled manner.
	2) Place the feet hip-width apart and take an overhand grip on the bar a little wider than shoulder width, keeping your back flat.
	3) Straighten your legs and stand upright, with the barbell resting on your thighs. Now bend your thighs $1/4$ of the way down and bring your torso over your thighs and slightly above parallel to the floor.
	4) Allow the barbell to hang from your arms at full extension whilst breathing out. Now pull the bar up and into your lower abdominal region whilst breathing in and looking forward throughout the entire movement.
	5) Finish by lowering the bar back down your legs so that your arms are fully extended, stretching the back muscles again whilst you breathe out.
	6) Ensure you fully stretch the Latissimus muscles at the bottom of the movement, and throw the chest forward and shoulders back at the top of the movement to gain the maximum muscular contraction.
	7) Only undertake this exercise if your back is sound and injury free.

Start Position:

Stance Position:

Finish Position:

PULLOVER MACHINE

THE SCIENCE

Muscles used:	
Primary:	The major back muscles (Latissimus Dorsi) in conjuction with to a lesser degree the Tricep arm muscles.
Secondary:	Serratus Anterior, lower chest (Pectoralis Major and Minor) muscles, and the Teres Major, Teres Minor and Infraspinatus muscles.
The Result:	An isolation exercise for shaping and toning the Latissimus muscles.
Who Is It For? Men + Women:	Involved in muscle toning, endurance and bodybuilding exercise programmes.
The Training Zone:	Muscle Tone: 2-3 sets of 12-15 reps. Endurance: 3 sets of 15-25 reps or 25-50 reps Elite level. Bodybuilding: 4-6 sets of 8-12 reps.

THE ACTION

How To Do It:	1) Select a weight which allows you to perform your target Training Zone in a safe and controlled manner.
	2) Adjust seat height so that your shoulders are in line with the pivot point of the machine arm.
	3) Fasten the seat belt.
	4) Press the foot lever down and take a grip onto the handle bar, enabling you to place your elbows onto the pads provided.
	5) Release the foot lever taking the strain onto the arms.
	6) Now breathe out as you pull the handle bar down to your lower abdominal region.
	7) Slowly return the handle bar up as far as comfortable whilst breathing in.

Start Position:

Finish Position:

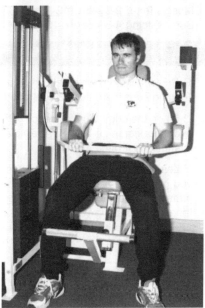

DUMBELL PULLOVER

Muscles used:	
Primary:	The major back muscles (Latissimus Dorsi) in conjunction with to a lesser degree the Tricep arm muscles.
Secondary:	Serratus Anterior, lower chest (Pectoralis Major and Minor) muscles, and Teres Major, Teres Minor and Infraspinatus muscles.
The Result:	An isolation exercise for shaping the Latissimus muscles.
Who is it for?: Men + Women:	Involved in muscle toning and/or bodybuilding exercise programmes.
The Training Zone:	Muscle Tone: 2-3 sets of 12-15 reps. Bodybuilding: 4-6 sets of 8-12 reps.

THE ACTION

How To Do It:	1) Select a weight which allows you to perform your target Training Zone in a safe and controlled manner.
	2) Sit on the edge of a flat bench with your palms facing flat over the inside of the dumbell plates with your thumbs interlocking around the handle.
	3) Lean back and lay flat on the bench, tilting the dumbell as you go, so it is now positioned above your head with your arms extended and locked in a slightly bent position. Keeping the elbows bent, lower the dumbell down backwards whilst breathing in to stretch the back muscles before returning the dumbell upwards to a point over your head as you breathe out.

Start Position:

Finish Position:

BARBELL PULLOVER

THE SCIENCE

Muscles used:	
Primary:	The major back muscles (Latissimus Dorsi) in conjuction with to a lesser degree the Tricep arm muscles.
Secondary:	Serratus Anterior, lower chest (Pectoralis Major and Minor) muscles, and Teres Major, Teres Minor and Infraspinatus muscles.
The Result:	An isolation exercise for shaping the Latissimus back muscles.
Who Is It For? Men + Women:	Involved in bodybuilding exercise programmes.
The Training Zone:	Bodybuilding: 4-6 sets of 8-12 reps.

THE ACTION

How To Do It:	1) Select a weight which allows you to perform your target Training Zone in a safe and controlled manner.
	2) Lie back onto a flat bench with the palms of your hands approx 10-15 inches apart on the barbell.
	3) Keeping your back flat, slowly allow your hands to lower the bar behind your head and below the back of the bench to stretch the back muscles whilst breathing in and keeping the elbows slightly bent and locked throughout the entire exercise movement.
	4) At the point of maximum stretch, begin to breathe out and return the barbell upwards to a point above your forehead with your elbows still bent and locked allowing you to come back to your starting point of the exercise.
	5) The same result and techniques will apply if you use a straight bar attached to the low cable pulley.

Start Position:

Finish Position:

BACK EXTENSION MACHINE

THE SCIENCE

Muscles used:	
Primary:	The lower back (Erectus Spinae) muscles.
Secondary:	The lower Oblique (Obliquus Internus) muscles and part of the Gluteal (Gluteus Medius) muscles.
The Result:	A safe exercise for providing lower back conditioning work.
Who Is It For? Men + Women:	An excellent exercise requiring minimal technical ability, suitable for general and specialist trainers.
The Training Zone:	Muscle Tone: 2-3 sets of 12-15 reps. Strength: 3 sets of 10 reps. Bodybuilding: 4-6 sets of 8-12 reps.

THE ACTION

How To Do It:	1) Select a weight which allows you to perform your target Training Zone in a safe and controlled manner.
	2) Adjust the seat height so that the pivot arm pads rest across your upper back/ shoulder line.
	3) Place the feet flat onto the footplate and secure the safety bar or belt across your thighs.
	4) Lean back and press against the pivot arm pads whilst breathing out, going as far back as comfortable.
	5) Slowly return back to the starting position whilst breathing in.
	6) Ensure on the backwards movement that you take care **NOT TO JAR YOUR LOWER BACK BY HYPER-EXTENDING.**

Start Position:

Finish Position:

PRIMARY & SECONDARY MUSCLES

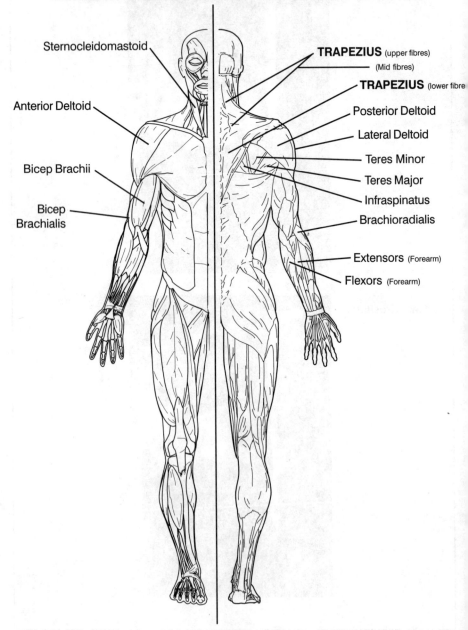

Sternocleidomastoid

TRAPEZIUS (upper fibres)

(Mid fibres)

TRAPEZIUS (lower fibre

Anterior Deltoid

Posterior Deltoid

Lateral Deltoid

Teres Minor

Bicep Brachii

Teres Major

Infraspinatus

Bicep
Brachialis

Brachioradialis

Extensors (Forearm)

Flexors (Forearm)

NECK
EXERCISES

WIDE GRIP UPRIGHT ROWS

THE SCIENCE

Muscles used:	
Primary:	The Trapezius neck muscles with some assistance from the side shoulder (Lateral Deltoid) muscles.
Secondary:	The front and rear shoulders (Anterior & Posterior Deltoid) muscles, Bicep arm (Brachialis and Brachii) muscles, and forearm (Flexor) muscles.
The Result:	Involved in bodybuilding exercise programmes.
Who Is It For? Men + Women:	Requiring additional neck development and strength for lifting a weight upwards.
The Training Zone:	Bodybuilding: 4-6 sets of 8-12 reps.

THE ACTION

How To Do It:	1) Select a weight which allows you to perform your target Training Zone in a safe and controlled manner.
	2) Take an overhand grip approx. one hand width past your shoulder width on the barbell, standing upright with a flat back and the feet approximately hip-width apart.
	3) Begin with the palms of your hands resting on your thighs with your arms fully extended as you breathe in.
	4) Whilst breathing out and looking straight ahead, draw the barbell close up the front of your torso, until your upper arms are parallel to the ground.
	5) Ensure your arms are fully in-line with the sides of your body throughout the entire movement.
	6) Slowly lower the bar back down to the starting position as you breathe in.
	7) By turning sideways on to a wall mirror, you will be able to check your execution of this advanced exercise.

Start Position:

Finish Position:

BARBELL UPRIGHT ROWS

THE SCIENCE

Muscles used:	
Primary:	The Trapezius neck muscles with some assistance from the side shoulder (Lateral Deltoid) muscles.
Secondary:	The front and rear shoulder (Anterior & Posterior Deltoid) muscles, Bicep arm (Brachialis and Brachii) muscles, and forearm (Flexor) muscles.
The Result:	An exercise to strengthen the shoulder girdle and develop the Trapezius neck muscles.
Who Is It For? Men + Women:	Requiring additional neck development and strength for lifting a weight upwards.
The Training Zone:	Strength: 3 sets of 10 reps. Bodybuilding: 4-6 sets of 8-12 reps.

THE ACTION

How To Do It:	1) Select a weight which allows you to perform your target Training Zone in a safe and controlled manner.
	2) Take an overhand grip approximately 8-10 inches apart on the barbell, standing upright with a flat back and the feet approximately hip-width apart.
	3) Begin with the palms of your hands resting on your thighs with your arms fully extended as you breathe in.
	4) Whilst breathing out and looking straight ahead, draw the barbell up the front of your torso, allowing your elbows to flare out at the top of the movement with the finishing point being where your elbows are slightly higher than your shoulder line.
	5) Slowly lower the bar back down to the starting position as you breathe in.

Start Position:

Finish Position:

CABLE UPRIGHT ROWS

THE SCIENCE

Muscles used:	
Primary:	The Trapezius neck muscles with some assistance from the side shoulder (Lateral Deltoid) muscles.
Secondary:	The front and rear shoulders (Anterior & Posterior Deltoid) muscles, Bicep arm (Brachialis and Brachii) muscles, and forearm (Flexor) muscles.
The Result:	An exercise to strengthen the shoulder girdle and develop the Trapezius neck muscles.
Who Is It For? Men + Women:	Requiring a conditioning exercise for the neck and shoulder area combined.
The Training Zone:	Muscle Tone: 2-3 sets of 12-15 reps. Strength: 3 sets of 10 reps. Bodybuilding:4-6 sets of 8-12 reps.

THE ACTION

How To Do It:	1) Select a weight which allows you to perform your target Training Zone in a safe and controlled manner.
	2) Place a straight bar onto the low pulley cable, and take an overhand grip slightly inside your shoulder width.
	3) Now stand up straight and keep your back flat, with your arms hanging down in front of you and the bar resting on your thighs, with your feet hip-width apart.
	4) Keeping the bar and palms of your hands close to your body, draw them up to above mid-chest height, allowing the elbows to flare out to the sides whilst you breathe out with the finishing point being where your elbows are slightly higher than your shoulder line.
	5) Slowly lower the bar back down to the starting position as you breathe in.

Start Position:

Finish Position:

BARBELL SHRUGS

THE SCIENCE

Muscles used:	
Primary:	The Trapezius neck muscles.
Secondary:	The rear and side shoulder (Posterior and Lateral Deltoid) muscles, in conjuction with the forearm (Flexor) muscles and the Bicep arm muscles.
The Result::	A strength and bodybuilding exercise for the Trapezius neck muscles.
Who Is It For? Men + Women:	Involved in strength building and bodybuilding exercise programmes.
The Training Zone:	Strength: 3 sets of 10 reps. Bodybuilding:4-6 sets of 8-12 reps.

THE ACTION

How To Do It:	1) Select a weight which allows you to perform your target Training Zone in a safe and controlled manner. 2) Place your hands slightly wider than shoulder width apart onto the bar using an overhand grip. Now whilst keeping your back flat, straighten your legs and stand upright with the bar resting on your thighs and your arms fully extended at the sides of your body. 3) From this position lift the shoulders upwards to contract the Trapezius neck muscles as you breathe in and keeping the bend in the elbows to a minimum. 4) Slowly return back to the starting position whilst breathing out.

Start Position:

Finish Position:

DUMBELL SHRUGS

THE SCIENCE

Muscles used:	
Primary:	The Trapezius neck muscles.
Secondary:	Dependent upon movement execution, either the front or rear shoulder (Anterior or Posterior Deltoid) muscles, in conjuction with the forearm (Flexor) muscles.
The Result:	A strength and bodybuilding exercise for the Trapezius neck muscles.
Who Is It For? Men + Women:	Involved in strength building and bodybuilding exercise programmes.
The Training Zone:	Strength: 3 sets of 10 reps. Bodybuilding: 4-6 sets of 8-12 reps.

THE ACTION

How To Do It:	1) Select a weight which allows you to perform your target Training Zone in a safe and controlled manner.
	2) Standing upright holding a dumbell in each hand with your arms fully extended at the sides of your body, place your feet approximately hip-width apart.
	3) From this position lift the shoulders upwards to contract the Trapezius neck muscles as you breathe in and keeping the bend in the elbows to a minimum.
	4) Slowly return back to the starting position whilst breathing out.
	5) The dumbell will travel only a few inches up the sides of your thighs but to incorporate either the front or rear shoulder muscles, rotate the shoulders either forward or backwards at the top of the movement and as you lower back down to the starting position.

Start Position:

Finish Position:

REVERSE SHRUGS (SMITHS MACHINE)

THE SCIENCE	
Muscles used:	
Primary:	The Trapezius neck muscles.
Secondary:	The rear and side shoulder (Posterior and Lateral Deltoid) muscles, in conjuction with the forearm (Brachioradialis and Flexor) muscles, and to a lesser degree the Bicep arm muscles.
The Result:	A strength and bodybuilding exercise for the Trapezius neck muscles.
Who Is It For? Men + Women:	Involved in strength building and bodybuilding exercise programmes.
The Training Zone:	Strength: 3 sets of 10 reps. Bodybuilding: 4-6 sets of 8-12 reps.
THE ACTION	
How To Do It:	1) Select a weight which allows you to perform your target Training Zone in a safe and controlled manner.
	2) Standing upright, place your hands on the bar behind your body at a width slightly less than your shoulders with your feet approx. hip-width apart.
	3) From this position lift the shoulders upwards to contract the Trapezius neck muscles as you breathe in and keeping the bend in the elbows to a minimum.
	4) Slowly return back to the starting position whilst breathing out.
	5) Ensure that your body remains upright throughout the entire movement with a flat back.
	6) Look forward and up as you perform this exercise to minimise stress onto the neck.

Start Position:

Finish Position:

PRIMARY & SECONDARY MUSCLES

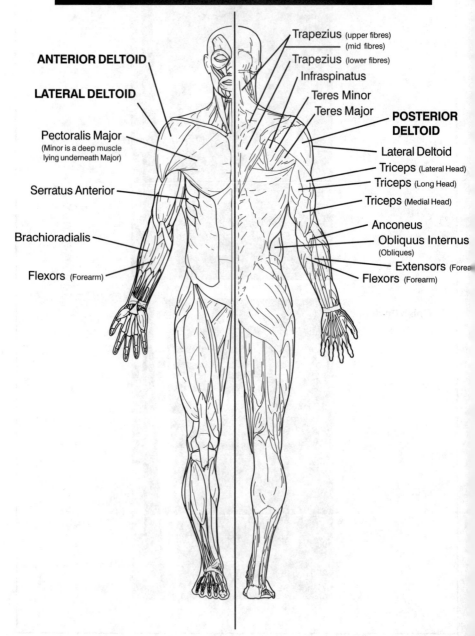

ANTERIOR DELTOID

LATERAL DELTOID

Pectoralis Major
(Minor is a deep muscle
lying underneath Major)

Serratus Anterior

Brachioradialis

Flexors (Forearm)

Trapezius (upper fibres)
(mid fibres)
Trapezius (lower fibres)

Infraspinatus

Teres Minor

Teres Major

POSTERIOR
DELTOID

Lateral Deltoid

Triceps (Lateral Head)

Triceps (Long Head)

Triceps (Medial Head)

Anconeus

Obliquus Internus
(Obliques)

Extensors (Forea

Flexors (Forearm)

SHOULDER
EXERCISES

SHOULDER PRESS MACHINE

THE SCIENCE

Muscles used:	
Primary:	The front and side shoulder (Anterior and Lateral Deltoid) muscles assisted by the Tricep arm muscles.
Secondary:	The Trapezius neck muscles, Serratus Anterior, and to a lesser degree the forearm and Anconeus muscles.
The Result:	An all-round strength and mass-building exercise for the shoulder muscles.
Who Is It For? Men + Women:	An excellent exercise requiring minimal technical ability, suitable for general and specialist trainers.
The Training Zone:	Muscle Tone: 2-3 sets of 12-15 reps. Strength: 3 sets of 10 reps. Bodybuilding: 4-6 sets of 8-12 reps.

THE ACTION

How To Do It:	1) Select a weight which allows you to perform your target Training Zone in a safe and controlled manner.
	2) Adjust the seat height so that the machine handles are in line with your shoulders.
	3) Grasp the handles with a grip slightly wider than your shoulders, keeping your back flat onto the support pad.
	4) Breathe out whilst pushing your hands upwards until your arms are fully extended.
	5) Slowly lower the handle bars back down towards the starting position whilst breathing in.

Start Position:

Finish Position:

DUMBELL SEATED SHOULDER PRESS

THE SCIENCE

Muscles used:	
Primary:	The front and side shoulder (Anterior and Lateral Deltoid) muscles and the Tricep arm muscles.
Secondary:	The Trapezius neck muscles, Serratus Anterior, and to a lesser degree the forearm and Anconeus muscles.
Result:	An all-round strength and mass-building exercise for the shoulder muscles.
Who is it for? Men + Women:	Involved in strength building and bodybuilding exercise programmes.
The Training Zone:	Strength: 3 sets of 10 reps. Bodybuilding: 4-6 sets of 8-12 reps.

THE ACTION

How To Do It:	1) Select a weight which allows you to perform your target Training Zone in a safe and controlled manner.
	2) Sit on a bench with a back support and your feet placed firmly on the floor. Now pick up the dumbells and lift them up to your shoulder height, with your palms facing forwards.
	3) Push the dumbells up from the wide base of your shoulders to a central point above your head as you breathe out.
	4) Now slowly lower the dumbells down from the finishing point as you breathe in and finish at the wide base of your shoulders.
	5) This action will be similar to Dumbell Bench Pressing where you will also utilise the imaginary 'pyramid' technique.

Start Position:

Finish Position:

BARBELL PRESS BEHIND NECK

THE SCIENCE

Muscles used:	
Primary:	The rear and side shoulder (Posterior and Lateral Deltoid) muscles, assisted by the Tricep arm muscles.
Secondary:	The Trapezius neck muscles, Serratus Anterior and to a lesser degree the forearm and Anconeus muscles.
The Result.	A strength and mass-building exercise for the shoulder muscles.
Who Is It For? Men + Women:	Involved in strength building and bodybuilding exercise programmes.
The Training Zone:	Strength: 3 sets of 10 reps. Bodybuilding: 4-6 sets of 8-12 reps.

THE ACTION

How To Do It:	1) Select a weight which allows you to perform your target Training Zone in a safe and controlled manner.
	2) Begin by placing the hands a little wider than shoulder-width apart onto the bar, ensuring that your back is supported against a pad on the bench.
	3) Now slowly press your hands straight upwards as you breathe out, keeping your head tilted slightly forward so as to avoid contact with the bar.
	4) Lower the bar back down from full extension of the arms to a point where the upper arms are slightly below parallel to the ground as you breathe in.
	5) The bar should now be at a point mid-way between the middle of your head and your Trapezius neck muscles.

Start Position:

Finish Position:

BARBELL FRONT SHOULDER PRESS

THE SCIENCE

Muscles used:	
Primary:	The front and side shoulder (Anterior and Lateral Deltoid) muscles assisted by the Tricep arm muscles.
Secondary:	The Trapezius neck muscles, Serratus Anterior, and to a lesser degree the forearm and Anconeus muscles.
The Result:	A strength and mass-building exercise for the shoulder muscles.
Who Is It For? Men + Women:	Involved in strength building and bodybuilding exercise programmes.
The Training Zone:	Strength: 3 sets of 10 reps. Bodybuilding: 4-6 sets of 8-12 reps.

THE ACTION

How To Do It:	1) Select a weight which allows you to perform your target Training Zone in a safe and controlled manner.
	2) Begin by placing the hands a little wider than shoulder-width apart onto the bar, ensuring that your back is supported against a pad on the bench.
	3) Now slowly press your hands straight upwards as you breathe out, keeping your head tilted slightly backwards, so as avoid facial contact with the bar.
	4) Lower the bar back down from full extension of the arms to a point where the upper arms are slightly below parallel to the ground as you breathe in.
	5) The bar should now be at a point mid-way between the middle of your face and the upper part of your Pectoral chest muscles.

Start Position:

Finish Position:

LATERAL RAISE MACHINE

Muscles used:	
Primary:	The side shoulder (Lateral Deltoid) muscles.
Secondary:	The front shoulder (Anterior Deltoid) muscles, Trapezius neck muscles, and rear shoulder (Posterior Deltoid) muscles.
The Result:	An isolation exercise providing excellent shaping capabilities for the side shoulder muscles.
Who Is It For? Men + Women:	Involved in muscle toning and/or bodybuilding exercise programmes.
The Training Zone:	Muscle Tone: 2-3 sets of 12-15 reps. Endurance: 3 sets of 15-25 reps or 25-50 reps Elite level. Bodybuilding: 4-6 sets of 8-12 reps.

THE ACTION

How To Do It?	1) Select a weight which allows you to perform your target Training Zone in a safe and controlled manner.
	2) Adjust the seat height so that in the starting position the arm pads rest comfortably against your forearms / upper arms.
	3) Keep your back flat against the support pad.
	4) Breathe out whilst raising both arms / elbows outwards and upwards to the side of your body, stopping when they become parallel to the ground.
	5) Slowly return the arms back down towards the starting position whilst breathing in.

Start Position:

Finish Position:

DUMBELL LATERAL RAISES

	THE SCIENCE
Muscles used:	
Primary:	The side shoulder (Lateral Deltoid) muscles, and the forearm (Extensor) muscles.
Secondary:	The Trapezius neck muscles, the front shoulder (Anterior Deltoid), the forearm (Flexor) muscles, and the rear shoulder (Posterior Deltoid) muscles.
The Result:	An isolation exercise providing excellent shaping capabilities for the side shoulder muscles.
Who is it for? Men + Women:	Involved in muscle toning and/or bodybuilding exercise programmes.
The Training Zone:	Muscle Tone: 2-3 sets of 12-15 reps. Bodybuilding: 4-6 sets of 8-12 reps.

	THE ACTION
How To Do It:	1) Select a weight which allows you to perform your target Training Zone in a safe and controlled manner.
	2) It is recommended for maximum benefits from this exercise to either train with one dumbell at a time standing up or with two dumbells seated. Begin by having the dumbells at arms length sitting on the edge of the bench.
	3) Now drag the dumbells up slightly 2-3 inches and lock your elbows in this bent position.
	4) Raise both dumbells away from the sides of your body whilst you breathe out and finish at the position with your forearms parallel to the ground.
	5) Maintaining your elbows in this bent and locked position, lower the dumbells back down towards the starting position as you breathe in.

Start Position 1:

Finish Position 1:

Start Position 2:

Finish Position 2:

SINGLE ARM CABLE LATERAL RAISES

	THE SCIENCE
Muscles used:	
Primary:	The side shoulder (Lateral Deltoid) muscles.
Secondary:	The front shoulder (Anterior Deltoid) muscles, Trapezius neck muscles, forearm (Flexor and Extensor) muscles, and the rear shoulder (Posterior Deltoid) muscles.
The Result:	An isolation exercise providing excellent shaping capabilities for the side shoulder muscles.
Who Is It For? Men + Women:	Requiring a more technically advanced exercise for bodybuilding and strict-style training.
The Training Zone:	Bodybuilding: 4-6 sets of 8-12 reps.
	THE ACTION
How To Do It:	1) Select a weight which allows you to perform your target Training Zone in a safe and controlled manner.
	2) Place a stirrup handle onto the low pulley taking an overhand grip, stand up keeping your back flat bringing the cable in front or behind (advanced method) your body.
	3) Locking the elbow at a slightly bent angle, raise your arm out from the side of your body until your forearm is parallel to the ground whilst breathing out.
	4) Slowly return $^3/_4$ of the way back down to the starting position whilst breathing in and keeping continuous tension on the shoulders rather than the arm muscles.

Start Position 1:

Finish Position 1:

Start Position 2:

Finish Position 2:

DUMBELL FRONT RAISES

THE SCIENCE

Muscles used:	
Primary:	The front shoulder (Anterior Deltoid) muscles, and the forearm (Extensor) muscles.
Secondary:	The Trapezius neck muscles, Serratus Anterior muscles, forearm (Flexor) muscles and to a lesser degree the side shoulder (Lateral Deltoid) muscles, and the lower Pectoral chest muscles.
The Result:	An isolation exercise for working the front shoulder muscles.
Who is it for? Men + Women:	Involved in strength building and bodybuilding exercise programmes.
The Training Zone:	Strength: 3 sets of 10 reps. Bodybuilding: 4-6 sets of 8-12 reps.

THE ACTION

How To Do It:	1) Select a weight which allows you to perform your target Training Zone in a safe and controlled manner.
	2) It is recommended for maximum benefits from this exercise to train with one dumbell at a time. Standing upright with a flat back and the dumbell resting against your thigh with your arm fully extended, drag the palm of your hand up your thigh approximately 2-3 inches and now lock your elbow in this bent position.
	3) Whilst supporting yourself against a bench etc, with your free hand, now raise the dumbell up and away from your leg until your forearm is now parallel to the ground as you breathe out.
	4) Maintaining your elbow in the bent and locked position, lower the dumbell back down towards the starting position as you breathe in.

Start Position:

Finish Position:

DUMBELL BENT-OVER LATERAL RAISES

THE SCIENCE	
Muscles used:	
Primary:	The rear shoulder (Posterior Deltoid) muscles.
Secondary:	The Trapezius neck muscles, the side shoulder (Lateral Deltoid) muscles, and some upper back muscles, Teres Major, Teres Minor and Infraspinatus) in conjunction with the Latissimus Dorsi muscles to a lesser degree.
The Results:	An isolation exercise for working the rear shoulder muscles.
Who is it for? Men + Women:	Involved in muscle toning and/or bodybuilding exercise programmes.
The Training Zone:	Muscle Tone: 2-3 sets of 12-15 reps. Bodybuilding: 4-6 sets of 8-12 reps.

THE ACTION	
How To Do It:	1) Select a weight which allows you to perform your target Training Zone in a safe and controlled manner.
	2) It is recommended for maximum benefits from this exercise to sit down on the edge of a bench with your feet together and extended as far forward as comfortable, whilst remaining flat on the floor.
	3) Begin by having both dumbells on the floor underneath your thighs, and bend over so that your abdomen and chest are as close to your thighs as comfortable. Pick up the dumbells locking both elbows in a bent position, and now raise both arms up and out to the sides of your body allowing you to bring your shoulder blades together whilst breathing in and keeping your elbows locked in a bent position.
	4) Now slowly lower your elbows back down so the dumbells return to a position just above the floor whilst you breathe out.
	5) By keeping the head up throughout the entire movement, you will also incorporate the Trapezius neck muscles into the workload more effeciently.

Start Position:

Finish Position:

BENT-OVER CABLE LATERAL RAISES

Muscles used:	
Primary:	The rear shoulder (Posterior Deltoid) muscles.
Secondary:	The lower Trapezius neck muscles , the side shoulder (Lateral Deltoid) and some upper back muscles, Teres Major, Teres Minor and Infraspinatus) in conjunction with the Latissimus Dorsi muscles to a lesser degree.
The Result:	An isolation exercise for working the rear shoulder muscles.
Who Is It For? Men + Women:	Requiring a more technical exercise for bodybuilding and specialist training.
The Training Zone:	Bodybuilding: 4-6 sets of 8-12 reps.

THE ACTION

How To Do It:	1) Select a weight which allows you to perform your target Training Zone in a safe and controlled manner.
	2) Place a stirrup handle onto both low pulleys of the Cable Crossover Machine.
	3) Take an underhand grip with opposite hands to pulleys so that your arms are crossed over.
	4) With the knees bent slightly, now bend the trunk over until your chest is parallel to the floor.
	5) Keeping the elbows slightly bent and locked, allow your shoulders to draw back your arms, squeezing your shoulder blades together, whilst breathing in.
	6) Slowly return the palms of your hands underneath your mid chest line whilst breathing out until your hands cross back over with your palms in line with opposite front shoulder (Anterior Deltoid) muscles.

Start Position:

Finish Position:

STANDING CABLE REAR DELTOID EXTENSIONS

THE SCIENCE	
Muscles used:	
Primary:	The rear shoulder (Posterior Deltoid) muscles, in conjunction with the Trapezius neck muscles (mid to upper fibres).
Secondary:	The lower Trapezius neck muscles, the side shoulder (Lateral Deltoid) and some upper back muscles, Teres Major, Teres Minor and Infraspinatus), in conjunction with the Latissimus Dorsi muscles to a lesser degree.
The Result:	An isolation exercise for working the rear shoulder muscles.
Who is it for?: Men + Women:	Requiring a more technical exercise for bodybuilding and specialist training.
The Training Zone:	Bodybuilding: 4-6 sets of 8-12 reps.

THE ACTION	
How To Do It:	1) Select a weight which allows you to perform your target Training Zone in a safe and controlled manner.
	2) Grasp the stirrup handles on the top pulleys of the cable crossover machine in opposite hands, and step up onto a block or bench to bring your shoulders more in line with the pulleys.
	3) Starting with the elbows locked in a bent position with the right palm just past the left shoulder and the left palm just past the right shoulder, breathe in and pull your hands across your front, throwing back the shoulders to contract the entire rear shoulder and Trapezius regions.
	4) With your hands finishing just wider than the same side shoulder, now breathe out and return your hands to the starting position as at No.3 above.
	5) Ensure your elbows remain locked in a bent position throughout the entire movement, keeping the tension constantly on the muscles in use.

Start Position:

Finish Position:

PRIMARY & SECONDARY MUSCLES

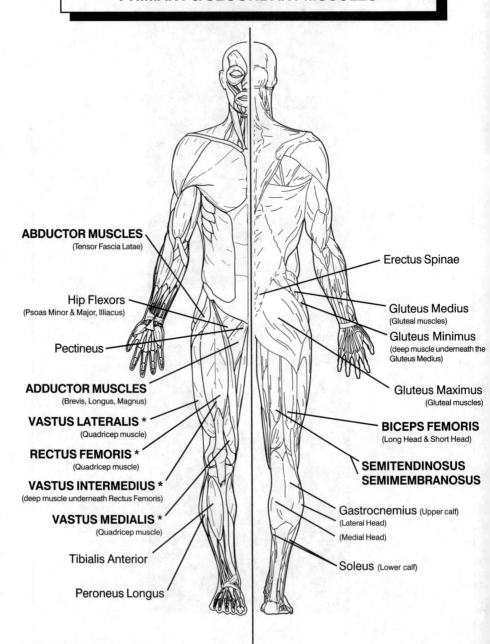

ABDUCTOR MUSCLES
(Tensor Fascia Latae)

Hip Flexors
(Psoas Minor & Major, Illiacus)

Pectineus

ADDUCTOR MUSCLES
(Brevis, Longus, Magnus)

VASTUS LATERALIS *
(Quadricep muscle)

RECTUS FEMORIS *
(Quadricep muscle)

VASTUS INTERMEDIUS *
(deep muscle underneath Rectus Femoris)

VASTUS MEDIALIS *
(Quadricep muscle)

Tibialis Anterior

Peroneus Longus

Erectus Spinae

Gluteus Medius
(Gluteal muscles)

Gluteus Minimus
(deep muscle underneath the
Gluteus Medius)

Gluteus Maximus
(Gluteal muscles)

BICEPS FEMORIS
(Long Head & Short Head)

**SEMITENDINOSUS
SEMIMEMBRANOSUS**

Gastrocnemius (Upper calf)
(Lateral Head)
(Medial Head)

Soleus (Lower calf)

LEG
EXERCISES

BARBELL LUNGES

THE SCIENCE

Muscles used:	
Primary:	The front thigh muscles (Rectus Femoris, Vastus Lateralis, Vastus Intermedius and Vastus Medialis) commonly known as the Quadriceps. Also the muscles of the inner thigh located just below the groin line (Adductors Magnus, Longus and Brevis) with some secondary assistance from the Gracillus and Pectineus muscles.
Secondary:	The Hamstrings, and Calf (Gastrocnemius and Soleus) muscles, Gluteal (Gluteus Maximus) muscles, Tibialis Anterior and Sartorius muscles.
The Result:	An exercise providing shaping and toning of the front thigh and Gluteal muscles.
Who Is It For? Men + Women:	Involved in muscle toning or bodybuilding exercise programmes.
The Training Zone:	Muscle Tone: 2-3 sets of 12-15 reps. Bodybuilding: 4-6 sets of 8-12 reps.

THE ACTION

How To Do It:	1) Select a weight which allows you to perform your target Training Zone in a safe and controlled manner.
	2) Begin by positioning the bar firmly onto the Trapezius neck muscles with the hands past shoulder width apart for stability and balance.
	3) Carefully take a medium stride forward with one foot and place your foot firmly on the ground.
	4) From this position, bend the leading leg in a squat action until the thigh is parallel to the floor and the knee of the trailing leg is now close to touching the floor, breathing in throughout this phase of the movement.
	5) Return to the starting position with the leading leg fully extended as you breathe out.
	6) After completing your target repetitions change over and utilise the other leg as the lead to provide an equal workload distribution.
	7) Ensure that the leading leg's knee region does not go over and in front of your toes - as this may cause severe stress onto the joints.

Start Position:

Finish Position:

LEG EXTENSION MACHINE

THE SCIENCE

Muscles used:	
Primary:	The front thigh muscles (Rectus Femoris, Vastus Lateralis, Vastus Intermedius and Vastus Medialis) commonly known as the Quadriceps.
Secondary:	The Sartorius, Tibialis Anterior and Hamstring muscles.
The Result:	An isolation exercise providing excellent shaping or building capabilities for the front thigh muscles.
Who Is It For? Men + Women:	Requiring an exercise using minimal technical ability, suitable for both general and specialist trainers.
The Training Zone:	Muscle Tone: 2-3 sets of 12-15 reps. Endurance: 3 sets of 15-25 reps or 25-50 reps Elite level. Strength: 3 sets of 10 reps. Bodybuilding: 4-6 sets of 8-12 reps.

THE ACTION

How To Do It:	1) Select a weight which allows you to perform your target Training Zone in a safe and controlled manner.
	2) Adjust the pads down the pivot arm so they sit above your feet and ankles when your knees are in line with the pivot point.
	3) Ensure that your back is flat against the support pad and grasp the handles firmly to assist you.
	4) Slowly raise your feet up lifting the pads until your legs are fully extended whilst you breath out , taking care **NOT TO JAR YOUR KNEES AT THE TOP OF THE MOVEMENT.**
	5) Return back down in the opposite direction towards the starting position whilst breathing in and keeping your toes pointed back towards your shins at all times.
NOTE:	**By pointing the toes back towards your shins throughout the movement this will increase the workload onto the legs.**

Start Position:

Finish Position:

SINGLE LEG EXTENSION MACHINE

THE SCIENCE

Muscles used:	
Primary:	The front thigh muscles (Rectus Femoris, Vastus Lateralis, Vastus Intermedius and Vastus Medialis) commonly known as the Quadriceps.
Secondary:	The Sartorius, Tibialis Anterior and Hamstring muscles.
The Result:	An isolation exercise providing excellent shaping or building capabilities for the front thigh muscles.
Who Is It For? Men + Women:	Requiring an exercise using some technical ability, suitable for general, specialist and rehabilitation training.
The Training Zone:	Muscle Tone: 2-3 sets of 12-15 reps. Strength: 3 sets of 10 reps. Bodybuilding: 4-6 sets of 8-12 reps.

THE ACTION

How To Do It:	1) Select a weight which allows you to perform your target Training Zone in a safe and controlled manner.
	2) Adjust the pads down the pivot arm so they sit above your feet and ankles when your knees are in line with the pivot point.
	3) Ensure that your back is flat against the support pad and grasp the handles firmly to assist you.
	4) Slowly raise up the foot of the leg that you wish to train, lifting the pad until the leg is fully extended, whilst you breathe out, taking care **NOT TO JAR YOUR KNEE AT THE TOP OF THE MOVEMENT.**
	5) Return back down in the opposite direction towards the starting position whilst breathing in and keeping your toes pointed back towards your shins at all times.
NOTE:	**By pointing the toes back towards your shins throughout the movement this will increase the workload onto the legs.**

Start Position:

Finish Position:

HORIZONTAL LEG PRESS MACHINE

THE SCIENCE

Muscles used:	
Primary:	The front thigh muscles (Rectus Femoris, Vastus Lateralis, Vastus Intermedius and Vastus Medialis) commonly known as the Quadriceps. Also the muscles of the inner thigh located just below the groin line (Adductors Magnus, Longus and Brevis) with some assistance from the Gracillus and Pectineus muscles.
Secondary:	The Hamstrings, and Calf (Gastrocnemius and Soleus) muscles, Gluteal (Gluteus Maximus) muscles, Tibialis Anterior and Sartorius muscles.
The Result:	An exercise providing excellent strength and mass-building capabilities for the front thigh muscles, but can also be used for general muscle toning.
Who Is It For? Men:	Requiring greater overall strength and development of the front thigh muscles.
Women:	Requiring increased muscle tone of the quadriceps in conjunction with the adductors.
The Training Zone:	Muscle Tone: 2-3 sets of 12-15 reps. Strength: 3 sets of 10 reps. Bodybuilding: 4-6 sets of 8-12 reps.

THE ACTION

How To Do It:	1) Select a weight which allows you to perform your target Training Zone in a safe and controlled manner.
	2) Adjust the flat carriageway so that when you are lying upon it with your shoulders against the support pads and your feet placed onto the footplate, your legs are not bent past a point of 90° in relation from the thigh to calf.
	3) With the heels hip-width apart, turn your toes outward slightly wider and press away from the footplate until your legs are fully extended while you breathe out taking care **NOT TO JAR YOUR KNEES AT THE TOP OF THE MOVEMENT.**
	4) Slowly return back to the starting position by bending the knees and keeping the heels flat onto the footplate whilst breathing in.

Start Position:

Finish Position:

INCLINE LEG PRESS MACHINE

THE SCIENCE

Muscles used:	
Primary:	The front thigh muscles (Rectus Femoris, Vastus Lateralis, Vastus Intermedius and Vastus Medialis) commonly known as the Quadriceps. Also the muscles of the inner thigh located just below the groin line (Adductors Magnus, Longus and Brevis) with some assistance from the Gracillus and Pectineus muscles.
Secondary:	The Hamstrings, and Calf (Gastrocnemius and Soleus) muscles, Gluteal (Gluteus Maximus) muscles, Tibialis Anterior and Sartorius muscles.
The Result:	An excellent exercise providing strength and mass-building capabilities for the front thigh muscles.
Who Is It For? Men + Women:	Involved in strength building and bodybuilding exercise programmes.
The Training Zone:	Strength: 3 sets of 10 reps. Bodybuilding: 4-6 sets of 8-12 reps. Powerbuilding: 3-5 sets of 1-6 reps.

THE ACTION

How To Do It:	1) Select a weight which allows you to perform your target Training Zone in a safe and controlled manner.
	2) Adjust the back support pad to an angle allowing you to comfortably place your feet flat onto the footplate whilst keeping your back flat on the pad.
	3) Press out with your feet until your legs are fully extended with your heels hip-width apart and your toes turned slightly outwards taking care **NOT TO JAR YOUR KNEES AT THE TOP OF THE MOVEMENT** whilst breathing out.
	4) Turn the safety handles outwards allowing you to slowly bend the knees and bring your thighs down to take you slightly below a 90° knee angle whilst breathing in.
	5) Slowly return back to the starting position by pressing the footplate away from your body whilst breathing out, ensuring the safety handles are engaged upon completion of your set.

Start Position:

Finish Position:

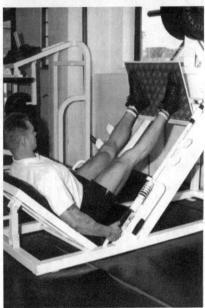

HACK SQUAT MACHINE

THE SCIENCE

Muscles used:	
Primary:	The front thigh muscles (Rectus Femoris, Vastus Lateralis, Vastus Intermedius and Vastus Medialis) commonly known as the Quadriceps. Also the muscles of the inner thigh located just below the groin line (Adductors Magnus, Longus and Brevis) with some assistance from the Gracillus and Pectineus muscles.
Secondary:	The Hamstrings, and Calf (Gastrocnemius and Soleus) muscles, Gluteal (Gluteus Maximus) muscles, Tibialis Anterior and Sartorius muscles.
The Result:	A more specialised exercise for the front thigh muscles, used to enhance both muscular separation and mass-building as a combined result.
Who Is It For? Men + Women:	Involved in specialised exercise programmes.
The Training Zone:	Muscle Tone: 2-3 sets of 12-15 reps. Strength: 3 sets of 10 reps. Bodybuilding: 4-6 sets of 8-12 reps.

THE ACTION

How To Do It:	1) Select a weight which allows you to perform your target Training Zone in a safe and controlled manner.
	2) Adjust the footplate as necessary to allow you to keep your feet flat onto it at the bottom of the movement.
	3) Press out with your feet until your legs are fully extended with your feet hip-width apart and your heels turned slightly inwards, taking care **NOT TO JAR YOUR KNEES AT THE TOP OF THE MOVEMENT** whilst breathing out.
	4) Release any safety handles allowing you to bend the knees bringing your thighs downwards until you are slightly below a 90° knee angle, whilst breathing in.
	5) Slowly return back to the starting position by pressing away from the footplate with your body whilst breathing out, engaging any safety handles upon completion of your set.

Start Position:

Finish Position:

THE SQUAT MACHINE

THE SCIENCE	
Muscles used:	
Primary:	The front thigh muscles (Rectus Femoris, Vastus Lateralis, Vastus Intermedius and Vastus Medialis) commonly known as the Quadriceps. Also the muscles of the inner thigh located just below the groin line (Adductors Magnus, Longus and Brevis) with some assistance from the Gracillus and Pectineus muscles.
Secondary:	The Hamstrings, and Calf (Gastrocnemius and Soleus) muscles, Gluteal (Gluteus Maximus) muscles, Tibialis Anterior and Sartorius muscles.
The Result:	An exercise providing strength and mass-building capabilities for the front thigh muscles, but which is also sometimes used for general muscle toning.
Who Is It For? Men + Women:	Requiring greater overall strength and development of the front thigh muscles, or; muscle tone of the Quadriceps in conjuction with the Gluteal muscles and Adductors.
The Training Zone:	Muscle Tone: 2-3 sets of 12-15 reps. Strength: 3 sets of 10 reps. Bodybuilding: 4-6 sets of 8-12 reps.
THE ACTION	
How To Do It:	1) Select a weight which allows you to perform your target Training Zone in a safe and controlled manner.
	2) Adjust the shoulders pads to a height of your front shoulders before you step onto the foot plate.
	3) Place your feet with your heels hip-width apart and your toes turned slightly outwards onto the footplate.
	4) Bend the knees whilst keeping your back flat and slide your shoulders underneath the support pads
	5) Now stand up whilst breathing out until your legs are fully extended, taking care **NOT TO JAR YOUR KNEES AT THE TOP OF THE MOVEMENT**.
	6) Slowly return back to the starting position by bending the knees and keeping your heels flat onto the footplate whilst breathing in.

Start Position:

Finish Position:

BARBELL SQUATS

THE SCIENCE

Muscles used:	
Primary:	The front thigh muscles (Rectus Femoris, Vastus Lateralis, Vastus Intermedius and Vastus Medialis) commonly known as the Quadriceps. Also the muscles of the inner thigh located just below the groin line (Adductors Magnus, Longus and Brevis) with some assistance from the Gracillus and Pectineus muscles.
Secondary:	The Hamstrings, and Calf (Gastrocnemius and Soleus) muscles, Gluteal (Gluteus Maximus) muscles, Tibialis Anterior and Sartorius muscles.
The Result:	An explosive-power development, strength and mass-building exercise.
Who Is It For? Men + Women:	Involved in weight lifting, power lifting, explosive sports, bodybuilding and strength training.
The Training Zone:	Strength: 3 sets of 10 reps. Bodybuilding: 4-6 sets of 10-12 reps. Powerbuilding: 3-5 sets of 1-6 reps.

THE ACTION

How To Do It:	1) Select a weight which allows you to perform your target Training Zone in a safe and controlled manner.
	2) Begin by positioning the bar firmly onto the Trapezius neck muscles with the hands past shoulder width apart for stability and balance.
	3) Carefully lift the barbell away from the squat rack pins and take a step away back from the frame, finishing with your feet slightly wider than hip-width apart and toes pointing out.
	4) Whilst breathing in, bend the knees and lower yourself down until your thighs are parallel to the ground before breathing out and returning to a full standing position with the legs straight.
	5) Ensure throughout the entire movement that you keep your back flat and keep looking forward and up to provide additional balance.
	6) Only undertake this exercise if your back is sound and injury free.

Start Position:

Finish Position:

ADDUCTOR MACHINE

THE SCIENCE

Muscles used:	
Primary:	The muscles of the inner thigh located just below the groin line (Adductors Magnus, Longus and Brevis).
Secondary:	The Gracillus and Pectineus muscles.
The Result:	An isolation exercise providing enhanced muscle toning.
Who Is It For? Men + Women:	Can utlise this exercise as a key part of their thigh toning routine or for specialist training purposes.
The Training Zone:	Muscle Tone: 2-3 sets of 12-15 reps. Endurance: 3 sets of 15-25 reps.

THE ACTION

How To Do It:	1) Select a weight which allows you to perform your target Training Zone in a safe and controlled manner.
	2) Sit comfortably onto the seat ensuring your back is flat against the support pad.
	3) Place your legs onto the support pads ensuring there is no pressure on the side of the knees.
	4) Move the hand lever to open your legs to a comfortable width and secure.
	5) Now bring your legs together whilst breathing out.
	6) Slowly return your legs back to the starting position whilst breathing in.
NOTE WELL:	**Excessive amounts of weight lifted on the exercise can result in groin injuries.**

Start Position:

Finish Position:

TOTAL HIP MACHINE
(HIP ADDUCTION)

THE SCIENCE

Muscles used:	
Primary:	The muscles of the inner thigh located just below the groin line (Adductors Magnus, Longus and Brevis).
Secondary:	The Gracillus and Pectineus muscles.
The Result:	An isolation exercise providing enhanced muscle toning.
Who Is It For? Men + Women:	Can utlise this exercise as a key part of their thigh toning routine or for specialist training purposes.
The Training Zone:	Muscle Tone: 2-3 sets of 12-15 reps. Endurance: 3 sets of 15-25 reps.

THE ACTION

How To Do It:	1) Select a weight which allows you to perform your target Training Zone in a safe and controlled manner.
	2) If the platform where you stand can be adjusted, be sure it is set to a height which puts your hip joint in line with the central pivot point when you are standing upright on the platform.
	3) Facing the machine, with the pivot arm point central to your body, adjust the pivot arm to an angle of approximately 4 o'clock when using the right leg or 8 o'clock when using the left leg.
	4) Now taking hold of the handles with your hands, lift your leg up and onto the outside of the pivot arm pad.
	5) Ensure the pad sits comfortably on or above the inside edge of your knee and breathe out as you bring your leg down to your supporting leg.
	6) Slowly return your leg back towards the starting position whilst breathing in.
NOTE WELL:	**Excessive amounts of weight lifted on this exercise can result in groin injuiries.**

Start Position:

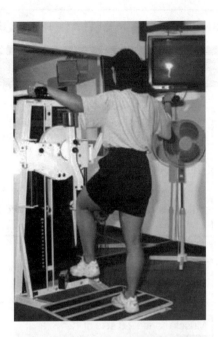

Finish Position:

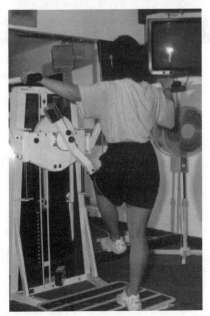

SINGLE LEG CABLE ADDUCTION

THE SCIENCE	
Muscles used:	
Primary:	The muscles of the inner thigh located just below the groin line (Adductors Magnus, Longus and Brevis).
Secondary:	The Gracillus and Pectineus muscles.
The Result:	An isolation exercise providing enhanced muscle toning.
Who Is It For? Men + Women:	Can utlise this exercise as a key part of their thigh toning routine or for specialist training purposes.
The Training Zone:	Muscle Tone: 2-3 sets of 12-15 reps. Endurance: 3 sets of 15-25 reps.

THE ACTION	
How To Do It:	1) Select a weight which allows you to perform your target Training Zone in a safe and controlled manner.
	2) Place an ankle strap onto the low cable pulley and over the ankle of your leg closest to the pulley when standing sideways on to the machine.
	3) Stand up keeping your back flat and take a sideways stride away from machine, bracing yourself against a bench on the side furthest away from the pulley.
	4) Keeping your body upright, draw your leg inwards towards your supporting leg and bench whilst breathing out and keeping the leg straight throughout the entire movement.
	5) Slowly return the leg back away from the side of your body towards the starting position whilst breathing in.

Start Position:

Finish Position:

ABDUCTOR MACHINE

THE SCIENCE

Muscles used:	
Primary:	The muscles of the outer thigh located just below the hip line (Tensor Fascia Latae).
Secondary:	The Gluteal (Gluteus Medius and Minimus) muscles.
The Result:	An isolation exercise providing enhanced muscle toning.
Who Is It For? Men + Women:	Can utilise this exercise as a key part of their thigh and hip toning routine or for specialist training purposes.
The Training Zone:	Muscle Tone: 2-3 sets of 12-15 reps. Endurance: 3 sets of 15-25 reps.

THE ACTION

How To Do It:	1) Select a weight which allows you to perform your target Training Zone in a safe and controlled manner.
	2) Sit comfortably onto the seat ensuring your back is flat against the support pad.
	3) Place your legs onto the support pads ensuring there is no pressure on the side of the knees.
	4) Now push your feet apart to a distance which is comfortable whilst breathing out.
	5) Return your legs together slowly whilst breathing in.
NOTE WELL:	**Excessive amounts of weight lifted on this exercise can result in adverse width-building of the hips.**

Start Position:

Finish Position:

TOTAL HIP MACHINE
(HIP ABDUCTION)

THE SCIENCE

Muscles used:	
Primary:	The muscles of the outer thigh located just below the hip line (Tensor Fascia Latae).
Secondary:	The Gluteal (Gluteus Medius and Minimus) muscles.
The Result:	An isolation exercise providing enhanced muscle toning.
Who Is It For? Men + Women:	Can utilise this exercise as a key part of their thigh and hip toning routine or for specialist training purposes.
The Training Zone:	Muscle Tone: 2-3 sets of 12-15 reps. Endurance:　3 sets of 15-25 reps.

THE ACTION

How To Do It:	1) Select a weight which allows you to perform your target Training Zone in a safe and controlled manner.
	2) If the platform where you stand can be adjusted, be sure it is set to a height which puts your hip joint in line with the central pivot point when you are standing upright on the platform.
	3) Facing the machine, with the pivot arm point central to your body, adjust the pivot arm to an angle of approximately 7 o'clock when using the right leg or 5 o'clock when using the left leg.
	4) Now taking hold of the handles with your hands, lift your leg up and across your body onto the outside of the pivot arm pad.
	5) Ensure the pad sits comfortably on or above the outside of your knee and breathe out as you push your leg down and across away from the side of your body to a comfortable height.
	6) Slowly return your leg back towards the starting position whilst breathing in.
NOTE WELL:	**Excessive amounts of weight lifted on this exercise can result in adverse width building of the hips.**

Start Position:

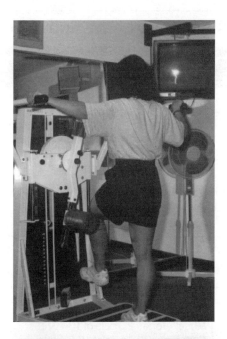

Finish Position:

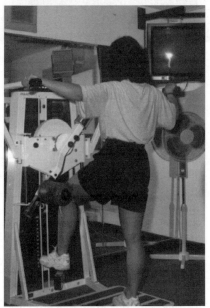

SINGLE LEG CABLE ABDUCTION

	THE SCIENCE
Muscles used:	
Primary:	The muscles of the outer thigh located just below the hip line (Tensor Fascia Latae).
Secondary:	The Gluteal (Gluteus Medius and Minimus) muscles.
The Result:	An isolation exercise providing enhanced muscle toning.
Who Is It For? Men + Women:	Can utilise this exercise as a key part of their thigh and hip toning routine or for specialist training purposes.
The Training Zone:	Muscle Tone: 2-3 sets of 12-15 reps. Endurance: 3 sets of 15-25 reps.

	THE ACTION
How To Do It:	1) Select a weight which allows you to perform your target Training Zone in a safe and controlled manner.
	2) Place an ankle strap onto the low cable pulley, and over the ankle of your leg furthest away from the pulley when standing sideways-on to the machine.
	3) Stand up keeping your back flat, the leg closest to the machine fully straight, and brace yourself with your nearest hand to the machine (keeping your hand clear of any moving parts).
	4) Keeping your body upright, raise your leg outwards to the side whilst breathing out, keeping the leg straight throughout the movement and taking the foot to a comfortable height.
	5) Slowly return the leg back down towards the starting position whilst breathing in.
NOTE WELL:	**Excessive amounts of weight lifted on this exercise can result in adverse width-building of the hips.**

Start Position:

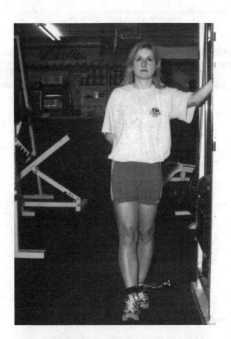

Finish Position:

TOTAL HIP MACHINE
(HIP FLEXION MOVEMENT)

THE SCIENCE

Muscles used:	
Primary:	The Hip Flexor muscles (Psoas Major, Illiacus).
Secondary:	The front thigh (Quadriceps) muscles. The Hip Flexor (Psoas Minor) muscles, Sartorius, and the lower abdominal (Transversus Abdominis) muscles.
The Result:	An isolation exercise providing enhanced muscle toning.
Who Is It For? Men + Women:	Can utlise this exercise as a key part of their abdominal toning routine or for specialist training purposes.
The Training Zone:	Muscle Tone: 2-3 sets of 12-15 reps. Endurance: 3 sets of 15-25 reps.

THE ACTION

How To Do It:	1) Select a weight which allows you to perform your target Training Zone in a safe and controlled manner.
	2) If the platform where you stand can be adjusted, be sure it is set to a height which puts your hip joint in line with the central pivot point when you are standing upright on the platform.
	3) Standing sideways-on to the machine, with the pivot arm pad adjusted to just above knee height, adjust the arm to an angle of approximately 7 o'clock.
	4) Now taking hold of the handle with your hands whilst facing sideways-on to the machine, push your lower thigh (Quadricep) muscles against the pad lifting upwards until your thigh is parallel to the platform whilst breathing out.
	5) Slowly return your leg back down towards the starting position whilst breathing in.

Start Position:

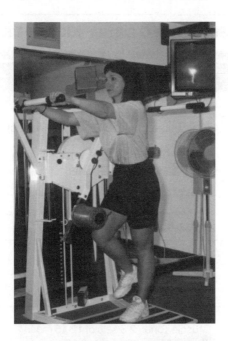

Finish Position:

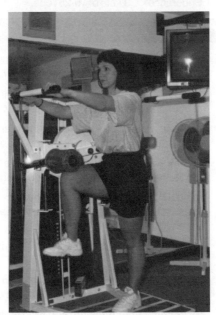

SINGLE LEG CABLE KICKBACKS

THE SCIENCE

Muscles used:	
Primary:	The Gluteal muscles (Gluteus Maximus).
Secondary:	The muscles at the back of the upper leg (Hamstrings), and the lower back (Erectus Spinae).
The Result:	An isolation exercise providing enhanced muscle toning.
Who Is It For? Men + Women:	Can utlise this exercise as a key part of their gluteal toning routine or for specialist training purposes.
The Training Zone:	Muscle Tone: 2-3 sets of 12-15 reps. Endurance: 3 sets of 15-25 reps.

THE ACTION

How To Do It:	1) Select a weight which allows you to perform your target Training Zone in a safe and controlled manner.
	2) Place an ankle strap onto the low cable pulley and over one of your ankles whilst standing face-on to the machine.
	3) Stand up keeping your back flat, bracing yourself against the machine, with your hands clear of any moving parts.
	4) Keeping your body upright , bend the knee of the strapped leg so that only your toe-end is touching the floor.
	5) Now from this position take the leg back as far as comfortable, keeping the knee slightly bent whilst breathing out throughout the entire movement.
	6) Slowly return the leg back down towards the starting position whilst breathing in.
NOTE WELL:	**Excessive amounts of weight lifted on this exercise can result in adverse mass-building of the Gluteal muscles.**
	By keeping your back flat you will reduce the possibility of increased stress onto the lower back (Erectus Spinae).

Start Position:

Finish Position:

TOTAL HIP MACHINE
(HIP EXTENSION MOVEMENT)

THE SCIENCE

Muscles used:	
Primary:	The Gluteal muscles (Gluteus Maximus).
Secondary:	The muscles at the back of the upper leg (Hamstrings), and the lower back (Erectus Spinae).
The Result:	An isolation exercise providing providing enhanced muscle toning.
Who Is It For? Men + Women:	Can utlise this exercise as a key part of their gluteal toning routine or for specialist training purposes.
The Training Zone:	Muscle Tone: 2-3 sets of 12-15 reps. Endurance: 3 sets of 15-25 reps.

THE ACTION

How To Do It:	1) Select a weight which allows you to perform your target Training Zone in a safe and controlled manner.
	2) If the platform where you stand can be adjusted, be sure it is set to a height which puts your hip joint in line with the central pivot point when you are standing upright on the platform.
	3) Facing the machine, with the pivot arm point central to your body, adjust the pivot arm to an angle of approximately 7 o'clock.
	4) Now taking hold of the handle with your hands whilst facing sideways-on to the machine, push your lower leg bicep (Hamstring) muscles against the pad and take the leg backwards whilst breathing out and flexing the Gluteal muscles (Gluteus Maximus).
	5) Slowly return your leg back towards the starting position whilst breathing in.
NOTE WELL:	**Excessive amounts of weight lifted on this exercise can result in adverse mass-building of the Gluteal muscles.**
	By keeping your back flat you will reduce the possibility of increased stress onto the lower back (Erectus Spinae).

Start Position:

Finish Position:

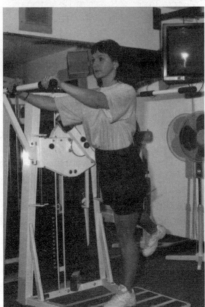

SEATED LEG CURL MACHINE

THE SCIENCE

Muscles used:	
Primary:	The muscles at the back of the upper leg (Biceps Femoris Long and Short Heads, Semitendinosus, Semimembranosus) commonly known as the Hamstring group.
Secondary:	The Gluteal (Gluteus Maximus) muscles and to a lesser degree the calf (Gastrocnemius and Soleus) muscles.
The Result:	An isolation exercise providing excellent shaping or mass-building capabilities for the back of the upper leg.
Who Is It For? Men + Women:	An excellent exercise requiring minimal technical ability, suitable for general and specialist trainers.
The Training Zone:	Muscle Tone: 2-3 sets of 12-15 reps. Strength: 3 sets of i0 reps. Bodybuilding: 4-6 sets of 8-12 reps.

THE ACTION

How To Do It:	1) Select a weight which allows you to perform your target Training Zone in a safe and controlled manner.
	2) Sit into the machine and adjust the back support pad so that when you place your legs onto the top of the pivot arm pad, your knees are in line with the pivot point.
	3) Tighten either the seat belt or thigh pad to hold you in place.
	4) Grasp the handles firmly to assist you in keeping your back flat against the support pad and ensure the leg pad sits behind your lower calf regions.
	5) Slowly "curl " your legs down bringing your heels towards you whilst breathing out and keeping your toes turned back towards your shins throughout the entire movement.
	6) Return back in the opposite direction whilst breathing in.

Start Position:

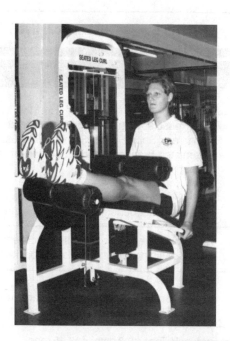

Finish Position:

LYING LEG CURL MACHINE

THE SCIENCE

Muscles used:	
Primary:	The muscles at the back of the upper leg (Biceps Femoris Long and Short Heads, Semitendinosus, Semimembranosus) commonly known as the Hamstring group.
Secondary:	The Gluteal (Gluteus Maximus) muscles and to a lesser degree the calf (Gastrocnemius and Soleus) muscles.
The Result:	An isolation exercise providing excellent shaping or mass-building capabilities for the back of the upper leg.
Who Is It For? Men + Women:	Involved in muscle toning, endurance, strength or bodybuilding exercise programmes.
The Training Zone:	Muscle Tone: 2-3 sets of 12-15 reps. Endurance: 3 sets of 15-25 reps or 25-50 reps Elite level. Strength: 3 sets of 10 reps. Bodybuilding: 4-6 sets of 8-12 reps.

THE ACTION

How To Do It:	1) Select a weight which allows you to perform your target Training Zone in a safe and controlled manner.
	2) Adjust the pads down the pivot arm so they sit above your heels when your knees are in line with the pivot point.
	3) Keeping the knees slightly bent, take the strain onto the legs as you lay face down onto the machine.
	4) Grasp the handles firmly to assist you in keeping your hips and torso in contact with the bench.
	5) Slowly "curl" your legs up behind you whilst breathing out and keeping your toes turned back towards your shins throughout the entire movement.
	6) Return back in the opposite direction whilst breathing in.

Start Position:

Finish Position:

STANDING LEG CURL MACHINE

THE SCIENCE

Muscles used:	
Primary:	The muscles at the back of the upper leg (Biceps Femoris Long and Short Heads, Semitendinosus, Semimembranosus) commonly known as the Hamstring group.
Secondary:	The Gluteal (Gluteus Maximus) muscles and to a lesser degree the calf (Gastrocnemius and Soleus) muscles.
The Result:	An isolation exercise providing excellent shaping or mass-building capabilities for the back of the upper leg.
Who Is It For? Men + Women:	An excellent exercise requiring some technical ability, suitable for general, specialist and rehabilitation training.
The Training Zone:	Muscle Tone: 2-3 sets of 12-15 reps. Strength: 3 sets of 10 reps. Bodybuilding: 4-6 sets of 8-12 reps.

THE ACTION

How To Do It:	1) Select a weight which allows you to perform your target Training Zone in a safe and controlled manner.
	2) Adjust the pads down the pivot arm so they sit above your heels when your knees are in line with the pivot point.
	3) Now keeping one leg straight, with your hips firmly against the support pads, "curl" your other leg up behind you whilst breathing out and keeping your toes turned back towards your shins throughout the entire movement.
	4) Return back in the opposite direction whilst breathing in.

Start Position:

Finish Position:

BARBELL STIFF-LEGGED DEADLIFTS

THE SCIENCE	
Muscles used:	
Primary:	The muscles at the back of the upper leg (Biceps Femoris Long and Short Heads, Semitendinosus, Semimembranosus) commonly known as the Hamstring group.
Secondary:	The Gluteal (Gluteus Maximus) muscles and the Erector Spinae muscles of the lower back.
The Result:	A highly advanced and specialised exercise for shaping, building and lengthening of the muscles at the back of the upper leg.
Who Is It For? Men + Women:	Advanced Trainers only: Involved in bodybuilding and specialist exercise programmes.
The Training Zone:	Bodybuilding: 4-6 sets of 8-12 reps.

THE ACTION	
How To Do It:	1) Select a weight which allows you to perform your target Training Zone in a safe and controlled manner.
	2) Take an overhand grip on the barbell, slightly wider than hip-width and step up onto a bench or high training platform.
	3) Slowly breathe out and whilst keeping your knees in a slightly bent and locked position, slowly lower the barbell down towards your toes whilst keeping it close in to your legs and maintaining a flat back.
	4) At a point of full stretch on the hamstrings, begin to breathe in and stand back upright slowly by drawing the bar back up close to your legs and straightening your trunk.
	5) Try to ensure throughout the entire movement that your arms remain as straight as possible and that you keep a slight bend in your knees to avoid additional lower back strain.
	6) Only undertake this exercise if your back is sound and injury free.

Start Position:

Finish Position:

PRIMARY & SECONDARY MUSCLES

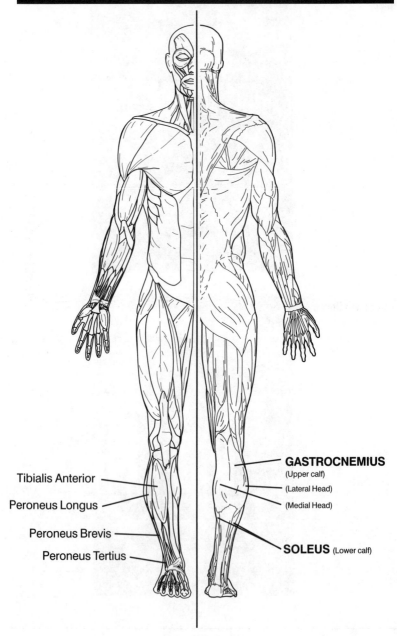

Tibialis Anterior

Peroneus Longus

Peroneus Brevis

Peroneus Tertius

GASTROCNEMIUS
(Upper calf)

(Lateral Head)

(Medial Head)

SOLEUS (Lower calf)

CALF
EXERCISES

STANDING CALF RAISE MACHINE

THE SCIENCE

Muscles used:	
Primary:	The upper calf muscle (Gastrocnemius Lateral and / or Medial Heads).
Secondary:	The lower calf (Soleus) muscle, Peroneus Longus, Brevis & Tertius and deep flexor muscles of the lower leg including Tibialis Posterior.
The Result:	An exercise providing excellent shaping or mass-building capabilities for the back of the upper calf.
Who Is It For? Men + Women:	Requiring greater overall calf strength or development, or a greater balance of the calf muscles plus increased ankle strength.
The Training Zone:	Muscle Tone: 2-3 sets of 12-15. Strength: 3 sets of 10 reps. Bodybuilding: 4-6 sets of 8-12 reps.

THE ACTION

How To Do It:	1) Select a weight which allows you to perform your target Training Zone in a safe and controlled manner.
	2) Adjust the shoulder pads to a height of your front shoulders before you step up onto the foot plate.
	3) Ensure the balls of your feet are securely on the footplate with your toes:
	a) Pointing straight ahead to work the entire calf region equally.
	b) Pointing outwards with your heels close together to concentrate on the inner (Medial) calf muscle.
	c) Pointing inwards close together and heels apart to concentrate on the outer (Lateral) calf muscle.
	4) Now stand upright straightening your legs whilst keeping your back flat.
	5) Raise your heels upwards as you breathe out and lower them back down as far as comfortable whilst breathing in.
NOTE WELL:	**The Achilles Heel tendon must be warmed up slowly to ensure that no injuries are sustained during this exercise.**

Start Position:

Finish Position:

SEATED CALF RAISE MACHINE

THE SCIENCE

Muscles used:	
Primary:	The lower calf muscle (Soleus).
Secondary:	The upper calf (Gastrocnemius) muscle, Peroneus Longus, Brevis & Tertius, and deep flexor muscles of the lower leg including Tibialis Posterior.
The Result:	An exercise providing excellent shaping or mass-building capabilities for the back of the lower calf.
Who Is It For? Men + Women:	Requiring greater overall lower calf development and ankle strength or a greater balance to compensate for a 'high' calf.
The Training Zone:	Muscle Tone: 2-3 sets of 12-15 reps. Strength: 3 sets of 10 reps. Bodybuilding: 4-6 sets of 8-12 reps.

THE ACTION

How To Do It:	1) Select a weight which allows you to perform your target Training Zone in a safe and controlled manner.
	2) Sit onto the machine and adjust the knee / thigh pads so that they fit firmly across your legs when your feet are on the footplate.
	3) Ensure the balls of your feet are securely on the footplate with your toes pointing straight ahead.
	4) Raise your heels upwards as you breath out whilst releasing the safety catch lever with your hand.
	5) Lower your heels back down as far as comfortable to enable you to stretch-out the calf at the bottom of the movement, whilst breathing in.
NOTE WELL:	**The Achillies Heel tendon must be warmed-up slowly to ensure that no injuries are sustained during this exercise.**

Start Position:

Finish Position:

DONKEY CALF RAISE MACHINE

THE SCIENCE

Muscles used:	
Primary:	The upper calf muscles (Gastrocnemius Lateral and or Medial heads).
Secondary:	The lower calf (Soleus) muscles, Peroneus Longus, Brevis & Tertius and deep flexor muscles of the lower leg including Tibialis Posterior.
The Result:	An advanced exercise providing excellent shaping and building capabilities for the back of the upper calf.
Who Is It For? Men + Women:	ADVANCED TRAINERS ONLY: Requiring this exercise for specialist and bodybuilding training.
The Training Zone:	Bodybuilding: 4-6 sets of 8-12 reps.

THE ACTION

How To Do It:	1) Select a weight which allows you to perform your target Training Zone in a safe and controlled manner.
	2) Adjust the lower back support pad to a height comfortable for you to be underneath when your feet are on the footplate.
	3) Ensure the balls of your feet are securely on the footplate with your toes pointing either straight ahead, inwards, or outwards, to give similar results as the Standing Calf Raise Machine.
	4) Ensure your forearms do not slip off the front support pad as you raise your heels upwards to lift the weight whilst breathing out.
	5) Lower your heels back down as far as comfortable whilst breathing in.

Start Position:

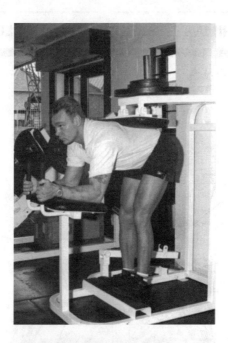

Finish Position:

PRIMARY & SECONDARY MUSCLES

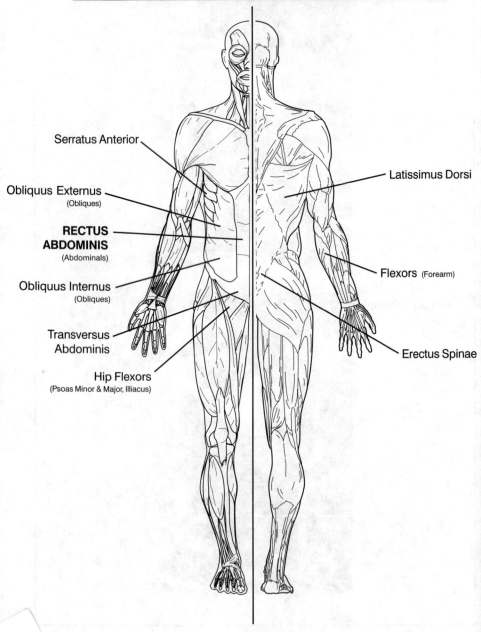

Serratus Anterior

Obliquus Externus
(Obliques)

**RECTUS
ABDOMINIS**
(Abdominals)

Obliquus Internus
(Obliques)

Transversus
Abdominis

Hip Flexors
(Psoas Minor & Major, Illiacus)

Latissimus Dorsi

Flexors (Forearm)

Erectus Spinae

ABDOMINAL EXERCISES

ABDOMINAL CRUNCH MACHINE

Muscles used:	
Primary:	The Abdominal muscles (Rectus Abdominis).
Secondary:	Part of the Hip Flexor (Psoas Minor) group and the lower back (Erectus Spinae) muscles to a lesser degree.
The Result:	An isolation exercise providing excellent conditioning of the abdominal muscles, with major emphasis being placed on the upper abdominals when the feet are at the front of the footplate, or the lower abdominals when the feet are placed underneath the rear pegs of the footplate provided.
Who Is It For? Men + Women:	Requiring a better-toned mid section.
The Training Zone:	Muscle Tone: 2-3 sets of 15-25 reps (or to reasonable failure). Endurance: 3 sets of 25-50 reps (or to reasonable failure).

THE ACTION

How To Do It:	1) Select a weight which allows you to perform your target Training Zone in a safe and controlled manner.
	2) Adjust the pivot arm pads to a height of your front shoulders once you are sat into the machine.
	3) Ensure the seat height is set to keep your hips in line with the pivot point.
	4) Now taking hold of the pivot arm handles bend forward pushing your shoulders against the pads until the arm goes down to your thighs whilst you breathe out.
	5) Slowly return back to the starting position taking care **NOT TO JAR YOUR LOWER BACK AT THE TOP OF THE MOVEMENT** whilst breathing in.
	6) By placing the feet onto the rear footpegs (if available) major emphasis can be placed onto the lower abdominals.

Start Position:

Finish Position:

ABDOMINAL CRUNCH

THE SCIENCE

Muscles used:	
Primary:	The Abdominal muscles (Rectus Abdominis).
Secondary:	Part of the Hip Flexor (Psoas Major and Illiacus) group.
The Result:	An isolation exercise providing excellent conditioning of the abdominal muscles with major emphasis on the upper abdominals.
Who Is It For? Men + Women:	Requiring a better-toned mid section.
The Training Zone:	Muscle Tone: 2-3 sets of 15-25 reps (or to reasonable failure). Endurance: 3 sets of 25-50 reps (or to reasonable failure).

THE ACTION

How To Do It:	1) Lie flat on the floor, or on an Abdominal Crunch bench, keeping your lower back in contact with the floor (or bench) throughout the movement. Place your feet under the foot pegs provided if using an Abdominal Crunch bench (see photo).
	2) Now draw your knees up to create a 90° angle with the floor (or bench), and breathe in.
	3) Place your hands at the sides of your head, and crunch up towards your knees whilst looking forwards and breathing out.
	4) Slowly return to the starting position without allowing your shoulders to come into contact with the floor (or bench), and breathe in.

Start Position:

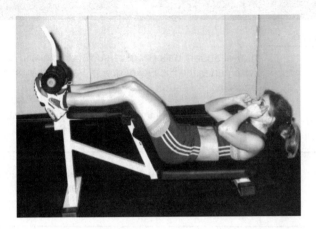

Finish Position:

ROMAN CHAIR HIP FLEXION

THE SCIENCE

Muscles used:	
Primary:	Lower abdominals (Transversus Abdominis) in conjunction with part of the Hip Flexor group (Psoas Major and Illiacus) muscles.
Secondary:	The Rectus Abdominal muscles in conjunction with to a lesser degree the lower back (Erectus Spinae) muscles.
The Result:	An isolation exercise providing excellent conditioning of the abdominal muscles with major emphasis on the lower abdominals.
Who Is It For? Men + Women:	Requiring additional toning of the lower abdominal muscles.
The Training Zone:	Muscle Tone: 2-3 sets of 15-25 reps (or to reasonable failure). Endurance: 3 sets of 25-50 reps (or to reasonable failure).

THE ACTION

How To Do It:	1) Ensure that your back is flat against the support pad by climbing backwards into the chair, using the foot pegs provided.
	2) Firmly grasp the handles and support your weight with your forearms remaining in constant contact with the support pads whilst breathing in.
	3) Now slowly breathe out as you raise your knees up to a 90° angle with the floor, whilst still looking forward.
	4) Slowly lower your knees back down towards the floor (not allowing your feet to touch the floor) whilst breathing in.

Start Position:

Finish Position:

LYING HIP FLEXION

THE SCIENCE

Muscles used:	
Primary:	Lower abdominals (Transversus Abdominis) in conjunction with part of the Hip Flexor group (Psoas Major and Illiacus) muscles.
Secondary:	The Rectus Abdominal muscles.
The Result:	An isolation exercise providing excellent conditioning of the abdominal muscles with major emphasis on the lower abdominals.
Who Is It For? Men + Women:	Requiring additional toning of the lower abdominal muscles.
The Training Zone:	Muscle Tone: 2-3 sets of 15-25 reps (or to reasonable failure). Endurance: 3 sets of 25-50 reps (or to reasonable failure).

THE ACTION

How To Do It:	1) Lie down on the floor, keeping your back in contact with the floor throughout the movement.
	2) Now draw your knees up to create a 90° angle with the floor, place your hands on the floor by the sides of your body and breathe in.
	3) Now slowly breathe out as you raise your knees towards your chest, keeping your buttocks in contact with the floor.
	4) Slowly return to the starting position, whilst breathing in.

Start Position:

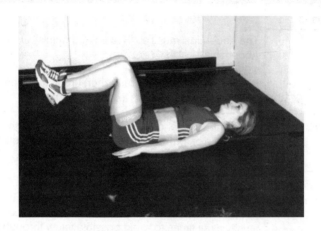

Finish Position:

CABLE CRUNCHES

THE SCIENCE

Muscles used:	
Primary:	The Abdominal muscles (Rectus Abdominis), Transversus Abdominis.
Secondary:	Part of the Hip Flexor (Psoas Minor) group and the lower back (Erectus Spinae) muscles to a lesser degree.
The Result:	Upper abdominal conditioning by kneeling in the "forward position", or primarily lower abdominal conditioning by kneeling in the three-quarter "sat-back" position.
Who is it for?: Men + Women:	Requiring an all-round abdominal exercise providing low stress levels on the back. NB: This exercise must be performed strictly at all times to avoid possible injury through incorrect body alignment.
The Training Zone:	Muscle Tone: 2-3 sets of 15-25 reps (or to reasonable failure). Endurance: 3 sets of 25-50 reps (or to reasonable failure). Bodybuilding: 4-6 sets of 8-12 reps (or to reasonable failure).

THE ACTION

How To Do It:	1) Select a weight which allows you to perform your target Training Zone in a safe and controlled manner. 2) Take a narrow grip on a flat bar or preferentially use the rope attachment. 3) Step back well away from the machine, pulling the rope down with you at chest height, and kneel down approximately four / five feet from the pulley base. 4) Select your kneeling position for either upper or lower abdominal work, placing the hands on the top of the forehead. 5) Now breathe out whilst crunching down until your forearms reach the floor. 6) Slowly return back to the starting position where the tension begins to leave the abdominals, taking care **NOT TO JAR YOUR LOWER BACK** whilst breathing in.

Start Position 1:

Finish Position 1:

Start Position 2:

Finish Position 2:

ROTARY TORSO MACHINE

THE SCIENCE

Muscles used:	
Primary:	The sides of the trunk-upper (Obliquus Externus) and lower (Obliquus Internus) commonly known as the Obliques.
Secondary:	The lower back (Erectus Spinae) muscles and the Abdominals (Rectus Abdominus).
The Result:	An isolation exercise providing enhanced muscle toning.
Who Is It For? Men + Women:	Requiring a better-toned mid section / hip and waist region.
The Training Zone:	Muscle Tone: 2-3 sets of 15-25 reps. Endurance: 3 sets of 25-50 reps.

THE ACTION

How To Do It:	1) Select a weight which allows you to perform your target Training Zone in a safe and controlled manner.
	2) Adjust the seat height so that the front rotary pad fits across your front shoulders (dependent upon machine design).
	3) Use the overhead release pin to allow the bar to be turned either left or right to the side of your torso.
	4) Grasp the two central handles crossing over your hands.
	5) Carefully bring the rotary bar around as far as comfortable whilst still remaining in contact with your front shoulders, and breathing out.
	6) Return back in the opposite direction towards the starting position whilst breathing in.
NB:	**CERTAIN MACHINES UTILISE A LOWER BODY ACTION RATHER THAN UPPER BODY SUPPORT PADS.**

Start Position:

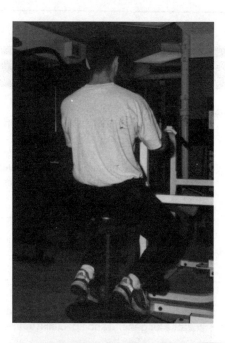

Finish Position:

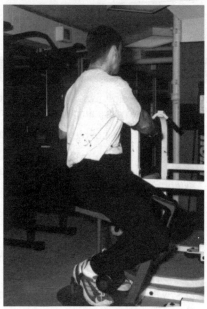

CABLE SIDE BENDS

THE SCIENCE

Muscles used:	
Primary:	The side trunk muscles (Obliquus Externus, Obliquus Internus).
Secondary:	The major back (Latissimus Dorsi) muscles - lower fibres, lower abdominals (Rectus Abdominis), Serratus Anterior, and forearm (Flexor) muscles.
The Result:	An isolation exercise to provide muscle tone to the sides of the trunk.
Who Is It For? Men + Women:	Requiring a trunk exercise needing minimal technical ability, suitable for general and specialist trainers.
The Training Zone:	Muscle Tone: 2-3 sets of 15-25 reps. Bodybuilding: 4-6 sets of 25-50 reps.

THE ACTION

How To Do It:	1) Select a weight which allows you to perform your target Training Zone in a safe and controlled manner.
	2) Place a stirrup handle onto the low pulley cable, taking an overhand grip.
	3) Stand up keeping your back flat, so that your arm is fully extended and slightly away from the side of your body with your feet placed hip width apart.
	4) Keeping the elbow straight, place your free hand at the side of your face, bending towards the side of your body.
	5) As you take your free elbow down towards the side of your trunk, breathe out.
	6) Slowly return back up to an upright position whilst breathing in.

Start Position:

Finish Position:

DUMBELL SIDE BENDS

THE SCIENCE

Muscles used:	
Primary:	The side lower trunk muscles (Obliquus Internus) muscles.
Secondary:	The major back (Latissimus Dorsi) muscles - lower fibres, lower abdominals (Rectus Abdominis), Serratus Anterior, and forearm (Flexor) muscles.
The Result:	An isolation exercise to provide muscle tone to the sides of the trunk.
Who Is It For? Men + Women:	Requiring a trunk exercise needing minimal technical ability, suitable for general and specialist trainers.
The Training Zone:	Muscle Tone: 2-3 sets of 15-25 reps. Bodybuilding: 4-6 sets of 25-50 reps.

THE ACTION

How To Do It:	1) Select a weight which allows you to perform your target Training Zone in a safe and controlled manner.
	2) Standing upright, holding one dumbell with your arm fully extended at the side of your body, place your feet approximately hip width apart, and your free hand at the side of your head.
	3) From this position, bend to the side with your free arm's elbow travelling towards the side of your trunk oppostite to the hand holding the dumbell as you breathe out.
	4) Slowly return back to the upright starting position whilst breathing in, ensuring that the arm holding the dumbell remains at the side of your body throughout the entire movement.

Start Position:

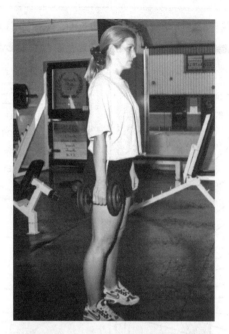

Finish Position:

PRIMARY & SECONDARY MUSCLES

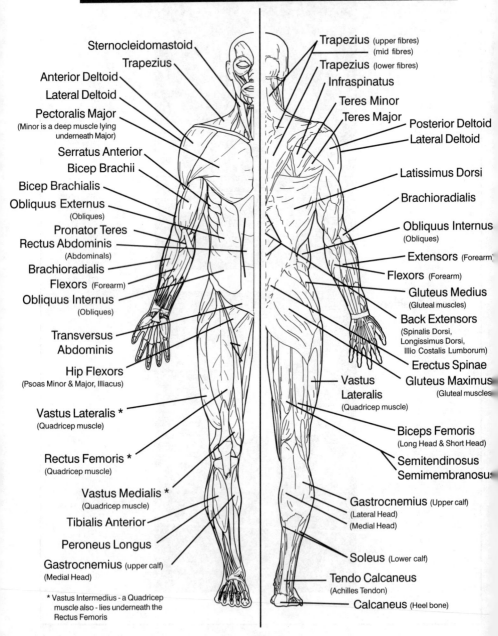

Sternocleidomastoid
Trapezius
Anterior Deltoid
Lateral Deltoid
Pectoralis Major
(Minor is a deep muscle lying underneath Major)
Serratus Anterior
Bicep Brachii
Bicep Brachialis
Obliquus Externus (Obliques)
Pronator Teres
Rectus Abdominis (Abdominals)
Brachioradialis
Flexors (Forearm)
Obliquus Internus (Obliques)
Transversus Abdominis
Hip Flexors
(Psoas Minor & Major, Illiacus)
Vastus Lateralis *
(Quadricep muscle)
Rectus Femoris *
(Quadricep muscle)
Vastus Medialis *
(Quadricep muscle)
Tibialis Anterior
Peroneus Longus
Gastrocnemius (upper calf)
(Medial Head)

* Vastus Intermedius - a Quadricep muscle also - lies underneath the Rectus Femoris

Trapezius (upper fibres)
(mid fibres)
Trapezius (lower fibres)
Infraspinatus
Teres Minor
Teres Major
Posterior Deltoid
Lateral Deltoid
Latissimus Dorsi
Brachioradialis
Obliquus Internus (Obliques)
Extensors (Forearm)
Flexors (Forearm)
Gluteus Medius
(Gluteal muscles)
Back Extensors
(Spinalis Dorsi, Longissimus Dorsi, Illio Costalis Lumborum)
Erectus Spinae
Gluteus Maximus
(Gluteal muscles)
Vastus Lateralis
(Quadricep muscle)
Biceps Femoris
(Long Head & Short Head)
Semitendinosus
Semimembranosus
Gastrocnemius (Upper calf)
(Lateral Head)
(Medial Head)
Soleus (Lower calf)
Tendo Calcaneus
(Achilles Tendon)
Calcaneus (Heel bone)

ADVANCED EXERCISES

BARBELL DEADLIFTS

THE SCIENCE

Muscles used:	All main arm, leg, shoulder and back muscles are utilised during the execution of this movement plus the Abdominal (Rectus Abdominis) muscles also.
The Result:	An explosive power development exercise.
Who Is It For? Men + Women:	Involved in weight-lifting, power lifting, explosive sports and specialised sporting activities.
The Training Zone:	Strength: 3 sets of 10 reps. Power: 3-5 sets of 1-6 reps.

THE ACTION

How To Do It:	1) Select a weight which allows you to perform your target Training Zone in a safe and controlled manner.
	2) Squat down and take a Power Grip at approximately shoulder width on the bar with one hand being in the "overhand" and the other in the "underhand" grip position.
	3) Now roll the barbell in towards your shins so that your feet are at hip width apart and toes pointing slightly outwards are showing beneath the bar whilst you continually look forwards and up.
	4) Whilst breathing out begin to straighten the legs and pull the barbell up past the shins and knees as quickly as possible, at which point you should push your hips forward, shoulders back and chest out so as to allow you to fully straighten up with a flat back.
	5) Ensure that your arms remain straight throughout the entire movement, and you breathe in again before lowering the bar down towards the ground by bending the knees and the hips.
NB:	**ONLY UNDERTAKE THIS EXERCISE IF YOUR BACK IS SOUND AND INJURY FREE.**

Start Position:

Mid Position:

Finish Position:

BARBELL POWER CLEANS

THE SCIENCE

Muscles used:	All main arm, leg, shoulder and back muscles are utilised during the execution of this movement plus the Abdominal (Rectus Abdominis) muscles also.
The Result:	An explosive power development exercise.
Who Is It For? Men + Women:	Involved in weight-lifting, power lifting, explosive sports and specialised sporting activities.
The Training Zone:	Strength: 3 sets of 10 reps. Power: 3-5 sets of 1-6 reps.

THE ACTION

How To Do It:	1) Select a weight which allows you to perform your target Training Zone in a safe and controlled manner. 2) Squat down and take an overhand grip on the bar at approximately just wider than shoulder width. Now roll the barbell in towards your shins so that your feet are hip width apart, with your toes (pointing slightly outwards) now showing through beneath the bar whilst you continually look forwards and up. 3) Whilst breathing in, begin to straighten the legs and pull the barbell up past the shins and knees as quickly as possible, allowing the bar's own speed of movement to bring it up to chest height. 4) Rotate your arms and shoulders underneath the bar and squat back down underneath it, allowing the bar to rest across your collar-bones with your elbows pushed through and forwards as you straighten your legs to a full standing position whilst breathing out.
NB:	ONLY UNDERTAKE THIS EXERCISE IF YOUR BACK IS SOUND AND INJURY FREE.

Start Position:

Mid Position:

Finish Position:

APPENDIX

SAMPLE READY-MADE
FITNESS PROGRAMMES

SAMPLE READY-MADE FITNESS PROGRAMMES

- Within this section you will find sample fitness programmes, that have been designed to help provide you with a clear perception of how exercises can be assembled to construct a typical fitness programme.

- For your benefit, sample programmes have been included for male and female trainers at beginner and intermediate level, along with examples of typical strength training and bodybuilding regimes for more advanced trainers.

- The key thing to remember, is that these are merely **SAMPLE** programmes - and not the ultimate or only choices available. The sample exercises selected for these programmes have been chosen to concentrate on the key areas of the body that most trainers generally express and interest in gaining improvements on.

- Whenever undertaking a fitness programme, always remember to start where YOU can start, and not to set unrealistic goals too quickly. Real results through the science of weight training can only be successfully achieved through the application of sound exercise knowledge and good technique. When you put this combination together in the gymnasium environment, there's nothing to stop you from maximising your potential.

SAMPLE
MALE BEGINNER'S
PROGRAMME

The sample exercises selected for this programme have been chosen to concentrate on the key areas that many males express an interest in gaining improvements on.

The programme illustrated shows exercises for a total body toning workout.

NO.	EXERCISE	RESULT
1.	Warm-Up (Bike)	To increase the Body Temperature
2.	Bicep Curl	General Strength Increase
3.	Leg Curls	Hamstring Work
4.	Leg Extensions	Toning the Front Thigh
5.	Bench Press	Overall Chest Work
6.	Lateral Pulldowns	Overall Back Work
7.	Standing Calf Raise	Upper Calf Work
8.	Shoulder Press	Overall Strength Builder
9.	Tricep Pushdown	Overall Tricep Work
10.	Abdominal Crunch	Toning the Stomach
11.	Cool Down	To include Stretching

SAMPLE
FEMALE BEGINNER'S
PROGRAMME

The sample exercises selected for this programme have been chosen to concentrate on the key areas that many females express an interest in gaining improvements on.

The programme illustrated shows exercises for a total body toning workout.

NO.	EXERCISE	RESULT
1.	Warm-Up (Bike)	To increase the Body Temperature
2.	Tricep Extension	Toning Back of Arm
3.	Leg Curls	Hamstring Work
4.	Pec-Dec	Overall Chest Toning
5.	Leg Extensions	Toning the Front Thigh
6.	Lateral Pulldowns	Overall Back Work
7.	Adductor/Total Hip	Inner and Outer Thigh Toning
8.	Lateral Raises	Deltoid Shaping Exercise
9.	Calf Raises/Stretching	Shaping the Calf Region
10.	Abdominal Crunch	Toning the Stomach
11.	Cool Down	To include Stretching

SAMPLE
MALE INTERMEDIATE
PROGRAMME

At intermediate level, both male and female trainers are at a stage where more than one exercise per main body part can be incorporated into the schedule, to further target key body areas.

NO.	EXERCISE	RESULT
1.	Rower or Treadmill	Advanced Warm-Up Equipment
2.	Supination Curl	All-Round Bicep Exercise
3.	Bench Press	Overall Chest Work
4.	Incline Flyes	Upper Chest Work
5.	Leg Extensions	Toning the Front Thigh
6.	Leg Press	Strength Building for Thighs
7.	Leg Curls	Hamstring Work
8.	Lateral Pulldowns	Overall Back Work
9.	Close-Grip Seated Rows	Strength & Mass Back Building
10.	Shoulder Press Machine	Deltoid Strength Exercise
11.	Tricep Pushdowns	Overall Tricep Work
12.	Standing Calf Raises	Upper Calf Region
13.	Cable Crunches	Upper and Lower Abdominals
14.	Cool Down	To include Stretching

SAMPLE
FEMALE INTERMEDIATE
PROGRAMME

At intermediate level, both male and female trainers are at a stage where more than one exercise per main body part can be incorporated into the schedule, to further target key body areas.

NO.	EXERCISE	RESULT
1.	Rower or Stepper	Advanced Warm-Up Equipment
2.	Hammer Curl	Shaping Front Upper Arm
3.	Pec-Dec	Overall Chest Toning
4.	Incline Flyes	Upper Chest Work
5.	Leg Extensions	Toning the Front Thigh
6.	Lunges	Shaping the Front Thigh
7.	Leg Curls	Hamstring Work
8.	Lateral Pulldowns	Overall Back Work
9.	Single Arm D.B. Rows	Shaping the Back
10.	Lateral D.B. Raise	Deltoid Shaping Exercise
11.	Single Arm D.B. Extension	Toning the Back of the Arm
12.	Calf Raises	Shaping the Calf Region
13.	Hip Flexion	Lower Abdominal Work
14.	Cool Down	To include Stretching

SAMPLE STRENGTH PROGRAMME

This sample programme has been designed for the client who already has several months basic training behind them, and now wishes to concentrate upon strength increases rather than toning or fitness increases.

NO.	EXERCISE	RESULT
1.	Warm-Up (Rower)	To increase Body Temperature
2.	Bench Press	Overall Chest Work
3.	Bent Over Row or Deadlift	Back Power Exercise
4.	Leg Curls	Hamstring Work
5.	Upright Rows	Overall Torso Strength
6.	Barbell Curl	Bicep Mass & Strength
7.	Squats	Quadricep Strength Builder
8.	Shoulder Press	Deltoid and Arm Strength
9.	Close Grip Press	Tricep Strength Builder
10.	Standing Calf Raise	Upper Calf Work
11.	Abdominals	Mid Section Strength
12.	Cool Down	To include Stretching

SAMPLE
BASIC BODYBUILDING
ROUTINE

The fist step into split routines for an experienced intermediate trainer looking to move more into a bodybuilding regime - may incorporate a basic half-body per workout strategy.

WORKOUT 'A' ON MONDAY & THURSDAY. 'B' ON TUESDAY & FRIDAY

WORKOUT 'A'		
NO.	EXERCISE	RESULT
1.	Bike	Short Warm-Up
2.	Dumbell Flyes	Shape and Pre-Exhaust the Chest
3.	Flat Bench Press	Overall Mass Builder
4.	Lateral Pulldowns	Overall Back Work
5.	Seated Rows	Overall Mass & Shape
6.	Bent Over Rows	Mass Builder for the Back
7.	Tricep Pushdowns	Overall Tricep Work
8.	Close Grip Bench Press	Tricep Mass Builder

WORKOUT 'B'		
NO.	EXERCISE	RESULT
1.	Leg Extensions	Shape and Pre-Exhaust the Quads
2.	Leg Press	Overall Mass Builder
3.	Leg Curl	Hamstring Work
4.	Lateral D.B. Raises	Shape & Pre-Exhaust the Deltoids
5.	Shoulder Press	Overall Mass Builder
6.	Standing Calf Raises	Predominantly Upper Calf Builder
7.	Barbell Curls	Bicep Mass Builder
8.	Abdominal Work	Vary from Hip Flexion to Crunch Movements

SAMPLE
ADVANCED BODYBUILDING
SPLIT ROUTINE

A	EXERCISE	RESULT	B	EXERCISE	RESULT	C	EXERCISE	RESULT
1	D.B. Flyes	Chest Shape	1	Lateral D.B. Raise	Deltoid Isolation	1	Pullovers	Back Isolation
2	Flat press (BB)	Chest Mass	2	Military Press	Deltoid Mass	2	Front Pulldowns	Mass & Shape
3	Incline D.B. Press	Upper Chest	3	Bent Over Raises	Rear Deltoids	3	Bent Over Rows	Mass Exercise
4	Concentration Curl	Bicep Isolation	4	Leg Extensions	Quad Isolation	4	Seated Rows	Mass & Shape
5	Barbell Curl	Bicep Mass	5	Squat	Quad Mass	5	Pushdowns	Tricep Warm-Up
6	Leg Curl	Hamstring	6	Incline Leg Press	Quad Mass	6	French Press	All-Round Work
7	Stiff Leg D/Lift	Hamstring	7	Standing Calf	Upper Calf	7	Single Arm Extensions	Long Head Isolation
8	Hip Flexion	Lower Abs	8	Seated Calf	Lower Calf	8	Crunches	Mid to Upper Abs

WHERE TO FROM HERE?

Congratulations!

You have just read the most comprehensive weight-training book on the market for exercise choices. The knowledge you have gained from this book will only serve as an appetiser for what is about to come on the main course: **WABBA - The "Ultimate" Series.**

THE ULTIMATE INSTRUCTOR'S INDEX

A dedicated handbook featuring all the essential terminology that's used or likely to be encountered by the Fitness Instructor of the new Millennium.

REAL REPS - THE ULTIMATE BOOK

Coming soon - the definitive guide to high intensity weight-training and bodybuilding exercise techniques. Including: Strip Sets, Super Sets, Giant and Tri-Sets plus all the Advanced Training strategies presented in an easy to read format.

REAL REPS - THE ULTIMATE VIDEO

Explosive on-screen action of the high intensity training principles found in: **Real Reps - The Ultimate Book.**

EXERCISE INDEX